SAY, DARLING

Say, Darling

A Comedy About a Musical

by

RICHARD BISSELL
ABE BURROWS
and MARIAN BISSELL

BASED UPON THE NOVEL
BY RICHARD BISSELL

An Atlantic Monthly Press Book
Little, Brown and Company • BOSTON • TORONTO

Photographs by courtesy of Friedman — Abeles

ATLANTIC–LITTLE, BROWN BOOKS
ARE PUBLISHED BY
LITTLE, BROWN AND COMPANY
IN ASSOCIATION WITH
THE ATLANTIC MONTHLY PRESS

Published simultaneously in Canada
by Little, Brown & Company (Canada) Limited

PRINTED IN THE UNITED STATES OF AMERICA

Book by	Richard Bissell, Abe Burrows, Marian Bissell
Songs by	Betty Comden, Adolph Green, Jule Styne
Production designed by	Oliver Smith
Costumes designed by	Alvin Colt
Lighting by	Peggy Clark
Dances by	Matt Mattox
At the pianos	Colin Romoff and Peter Howard
Associate producer	George Gilbert
Directed by	Abe Burrows

Say, Darling was first presented by Jule Styne and Lester Osterman at the ANTA Theatre on the evening of April 3, 1958 with the following cast:

(*In Order of Appearance*)

MR. SCHNEIDER	Gordon B. Clarke
FRANKIE JORDAN	Constance Ford
JACK JORDAN	David Wayne
PHOTOGRAPHER	Jack Naughton
PILOT ROY PETERS	Jack Manning
TED SNOW	Robert Morse
JUNE, THE SECRETARY	Eileen Letchworth
SCHATZIE HARRIS	Horace McMahon
RICHARD HACKETT	Jerome Cowan
IRENE LOVELLE	Vivian Blaine
RUDY LORRAINE	Johnny Desmond
SIDEMEN	Wendell Marshall
	Peter Howard
CHARLIE WILLIAMS	Robert Downing
MAURICE, A PIANIST	Colin Romoff
ARLENE MCKEE	Wana Allison
JENNIFER STEVENSON	Jean Mattox
EARL JORGESON	Elliott Gould
CHERYL MERRILL	Virginia Martin
ACCOMPANIST	Peter Howard
SAMMY MILES	Steve Condos

REX DEXTER	Mitchell Gregg
BORIS RESHEVSKY	Matt Mattox
WAITER	Jack Naughton
MORTY KREBS	Walter Klavun
TATIANA	Jean Mattox
JOYCE	Kelly Leigh

ASSORTED MINOR CHARACTERS

SYNOPSIS OF SCENES

TIME: The present

Act One

Act Two

Act Three

ACT ONE

ACT ONE

Scene One

Council Falls Airport.
Several airline passengers are crossing. Mr. Schneider
enters, sets his bag down. Frankie Jordan enters.

FLIGHT ANNOUNCEMENT
(*As curtain rises*)
Northwest Airlines Flight Three-forty-five for Chicago and
New York, leaving in ten minutes from Gate A.

MR. SCHNEIDER

Hi, Frankie.

FRANKIE

Hello, Mr. Schneider.

MR. SCHNEIDER

I'm off to Chicago for a few days. Convention. Women's Knit-
wear Institute. Where you going?

FRANKIE

I'm not going anywhere. Jack's going.

MR. SCHNEIDER

Where is Jack?

3

FRANKIE
(*Stalling*)
Well, it's something about his ticket.

JACK
(*Entering*)
Boy, by the time these guys get you a ticket.

MR. SCHNEIDER
(*Seeing him*)
Hey, Jack. What are you trying to do, sneak out of town?

JACK
No.

MR. SCHNEIDER
Where you going, Jack?

JACK
New York.

MR. SCHNEIDER
New York? What you going there for?

JACK
Well, you know that book I wrote.

MR. SCHNEIDER
That's right, you did write a book, didn't you? Sorry I haven't read it yet.

FRANKIE
Well, apparently somebody in New York has. That's why they sent for Jack. They want him to make a play out of it.

4

MR. SCHNEIDER

A likely story. Better look out, Frankie. He's probably got some cute little trick on the string down there. Heh! Heh!

JACK

Heh! Heh!

FRANKIE

Heh!

LOUDSPEAKER VOICE

Mr. Schneider, please come to the ticket counter.

JACK

That's you.

LOUDSPEAKER VOICE

Mr. Schneider, please come to the ticket counter.

MR. SCHNEIDER

I'm coming, I'm coming.
                    (*He exits*)

JACK

Hope I don't have to sit next to him. All those silly questions.
           (PHOTOGRAPHER *enters*)

PHOTOGRAPHER

Hi, Frankie. Hi, Jack.

JACK

Hello, Harry.

FRANKIE

Hello.

PHOTOGRAPHER

My editor sent me down to get your picture.

JACK

Picture?

PHOTOGRAPHER

You're going to be immortalized on page two. They didn't tell me what it's all about. Where you going?

JACK

New York.

PHOTOGRAPHER

New York? What are you going there for?

JACK

Well, you know that book I wrote.

PHOTOGRAPHER

Yeah. I've been meaning to read it.

JACK

Well, these guys in New York want to make a play out of it.

PHOTOGRAPHER

That so? Mighty interesting. Now let's try a shot with your arm around Frankie. That'll do. Thanks very much. Have a nice trip, Jack.

JACK

Thanks, Harry.

PHOTOGRAPHER

'By, Frankie.

FRANKIE

'By.

(PHOTOGRAPHER *goes*)

JACK

Pictures. All this fuss. I don't know if anything is going to come of this.

FRANKIE

Now don't start getting nervous.

JACK

Well, honey, I guess I am taking this too big.

FRANKIE

Of course.

JACK

Hell, I'm not going to the end of the world. I'll be back in three days.

FRANKIE

That's right.

JACK

I'm just going to New York.

7

FRANKIE

Sure.

JACK

I wish I'd never written that damn book. I was doing all right. The sash and door business has been pretty good to us.

FRANKIE

Can't you forget the sash and door business for a few days?

JACK

I don't want to lose that job. I didn't like the look on Old Man Johnson's face when I asked him for the three days off. You know, he still swears I wrote my book on company time. I don't know what he'll do when he finds out about this play business.

FRANKIE

It's going to be wonderful, Jack. You'll see. Your first book is behind you, and soon your first play will be behind you, and then you'll probably write one hundred and sixty more.

JACK

Frankie, I love you.

FRANKIE

Naturally. I'm a sensational wife.
(PILOT *enters*)

PILOT

Hi, Frankie. Hi, Jack.

JACK

Hi, Roy.

8

PILOT

You two flying with me today?

FRANKIE

I wish I was. Jack's going alone.

PILOT

Oh. Where are you going, Jack?

JACK

New York.

PILOT

New York? What are you going there for?

JACK

I've been traded to the Yankees.

FRANKIE

It's about that book he wrote.

PILOT

Oh, yeah. You did write a book. I never did get to read it. I resigned from the Book-of-the-Month Club.

(*He goes*)

JACK

"Resigned from the Book-of-the-Month Club." He was probably blackballed. Well, honey . . . It's getting to be about that time . . . Gee, Frankie, do you think these guys really mean it about me writing this play?

9

FRANKIE

They're paying for this trip.

JACK

I guess you're right . . . If the kids want to use the outboard motor, tell them not to leave it on the boat all night.

FRANKIE

All right, dear.
(JACK *sighs, puts his arms around her*)

LOUDSPEAKER VOICE

Last call, passengers for Flight Three-forty-five. Now loading at Gate A. Now loading at Gate A.

JACK

Why do they keep saying Gate A? We only got one gate.
(*He kisses* FRANKIE)
(MR. SCHNEIDER *re-enters*)

MR. SCHNEIDER
(*He looks back at Jack*)

I wish I liked my wife.
(*He goes*)

CLOSE IN

10

The New York office of Hackett and Snow. Full stage.
Ted Snow is on stage dictating to his secretary, June.

TED

"The entire production will be capitalized at three hundred
thousand dollars. Individual units will be six thousand dollars.
We feel that this show will prove to be a very sound investment.
Mr. Richard Hackett, who is my co-producer, and who will direct
the show, has a fabulous record of success on Broadway." (*Going
on*) "To write the score, we are planning to secure the services
of Rudy Lorraine, who is famed for his many popular hits; and
to write the libretto, we are hoping to sign Jack Jordan, the author
of the original best-selling novel *Paddlewheel.* We feel Mr. Jordan is ideally suited to do this . . ."

SCHATZIE
(*Entering*)
Because we couldn't get anybody else.

TED

Never mind, Schatzie. I don't like that kind of negative thinking. You're supposed to be our press agent, and I think . . .

SCHATZIE

Okay, Boy Producer, okay.

11

TED

That'll be all, June.

JUNE

All right, Mr. Snow.

(JUNE *goes*)

TED

Now, Schatzie, you know I don't like that Boy Producer stuff. I may be younger than Richard Hackett, but I'm his partner.

SCHATZIE

Let me ask you a question. For my own personal curiosity, how did a top director like Richard Hackett ever go into partners with you?

TED

It was I who acquired the rights to Jack Jordan's book and Hackett liked it. In addition, I've done a good deal of work in the theater.

SCHATZIE

This is your first show.

TED

It is not my first show. It happens to be my second.

SCHATZIE

Ted, we have a rule in this business. We do not count *King Lear.*

TED

It was a beautiful piece of theater.
(*Starts getting razor ready*)

SCHATZIE

It was a bomb.

(TED *starts his razor and begins shaving.* RICHARD
HACKETT, *a tall, elegant-looking man, comes in, taking off
his coat as he enters*)

HACKETT

Good morning.

SCHATZIE

Hi, Mr. Hackett.

HACKETT

(*Looks at* TED. *Then, speaking like a schoolteacher*)
What are you doing?

TED

(*Stopping his razor*)
I'm shaving . . . got up late this morning. I had to go to El
Morocco last night.

HACKETT

Nobody *has* to go to El Morocco. Any word from the boy yet?

TED

No.

SCHATZIE

I'm waiting for him, too.

HACKETT

Give him time. He's coming all the way from Iowa.

SCHATZIE

From where?

HACKETT

Iowa.

SCHATZIE

What the hell was he doing way out there?

HACKETT

Believe it or not, he lives there.

SCHATZIE

Maybe I'll be able to get an item or two out of the rube angle.

HACKETT

Schatzie, I was born in Nebraska.

SCHATZIE

Oh gee, I'm sorry. Well, wherever this guy comes from, I hope he can cut the mustard.

HACKETT

This boy is good. I wanted him on the project months ago, but my learned colleague, Mr. Snow, felt that we needed a "Name" . . . whatever that is.

(JACK *enters, stands there unnoticed*)

TED

Now, Dick, that's very unfair.

14

HACKETT

Well, go on, finish the other half of your face. I assume you
have brushed your teeth.

SCHATZIE

Hahoo!

TED

I have a right to shave in my own office.

HACKETT
(*Sees* JACK)

Who's that?

JACK
(*Pointing off stage*)
She said I should come right in. You're expecting me, I think.

TED

Mr. Jordan? I'm Ted Snow. Good to see you. And this, of
course, is Richard Hackett.

JACK

It's a great pleasure to know you, Mr. Hackett.

HACKETT

Glad you finally got here. I thought maybe you got lost in the
big city.

JACK

Gee, am I late? I'm sorry. But when I was coming down Fifth
Avenue, there was this excavation with a big crane. (*Getting*

15

excited) It was a Bucyrus-Erie one-twenty — big son of a gun! And there was this guy up on the boom. Man, he must have been eighty feet in the air.

TED

That so? And this is Schatzie Harris, the richest publicity man in the theater.

SCHATZIE

Not the richest, just the greatest. Good to see you, Jordan. How's everything out in Ohio?

JACK

Okay, I guess. I'm from Iowa.

HACKETT

Schatzie, they are two different states.

SCHATZIE

I know. I know Iowa. I was with an act in Boise once. That's Iowa, ain't it?

JACK
(*Shaking his head*)
Idaho. You see, Iowa is bounded on the east by Illinois and Wisconsin, on the north by . . .

TED

Don't explain it to Schatzie. He's never going there. (*Getting down to amenities*) How was the plane trip, Jordan?

JACK

Oh, pretty good, I guess. Got a little bumpy over Cleveland.

16

SCHATZIE

Now that's in Ohio. I know that.

HACKETT

Ted, let's get down to business.

TED

All right, Dick. (*He indicates a chair*) Sit down, Jordan, and we'll just give this deal a little rundown. (*To* HACKETT) Do you want to talk first, Dick?

HACKETT

No, go ahead, Ted.

TED

Cigarette, Jordan?

JACK

No, thanks.

TED

First of all, Jordan, let me say for all of us that we are very proud and happy to have acquired the rights to your fine book.

JACK
(*As though he were accepting a diploma*)
Thank you very much.

TED
(*Reaching for a cigarette*)
There is a certain wonderful quality . . . (*He stops talking as he lights the cigarette*) . . . about your material. Your stuff is

17

off beat, fresh. (JACK *pulls out of his pocket a bag of cigarette tobacco and cigarette paper and begins to roll a cigarette*) (*Going on*) Everybody here is pretty crazy about it. And, after all, when the Book-of-the-Month Club picked it for . . .

(TED *has finally become aware of the cigarette-rolling operation. He stops and stares. The others stare, too.* JACK *suddenly realizes he is being watched*)

JACK
(*Apologetically*)
I suppose it looks silly, but I've never smoked anything else. Uncle Orville — he's the fellow in the book — he taught me how to roll them when I was a kid and I've never smoked anything else.

SCHATZIE
(*Admiringly*)
Can you roll them with a filter?

JACK
Well, I never thought about that.
(HACKETT *has been looking at his watch. He now interrupts*)

HACKETT
Ted, let's get on with this. I'm playing squash before lunch. (*To* JACK) Do you play squash?

JACK
No, sir.
(HACKETT *grunts politely. It's a grunt that has gentle disappointment and disapproval in it*)

TED

Well, Jordan, I don't want to make a long speech, but the minute I picked up your book I had an immediate flash: "This is something I have got to do." Fortunately, I was able to communicate my enthusiasm to Mr. Hackett, who has consented to associate himself with me as producer. He will, of course, direct and assist you with the script and I have a firm conviction that . . .

HACKETT

(*Breaking in, his patience gone*)

Jordan, we think you can do this show. Do you?

JACK

Well, sir, that's what I came to find out . . . I mean, I think maybe I can . . . anyway, my wife seems to think so.

SCHATZIE

Your wife?

JACK

Yeah, Frankie. She's prejudiced about me.

HACKETT

Tell me, do you get to see many shows?

JACK

I suppose you don't count movies? (HACKETT *shakes his head*) Well, Frankie and I get to Chicago a couple of times a year to see the plays, and the Lunts used to come to Council Falls. I think it was the Lunts. Maybe it was Katherine Cornell . . . I never can tell them apart.

19

HACKETT

Jordan, your book has a quality that only you can transfer to the stage.

JACK

Well, if you want to take a chance on a guy who isn't really a writer . . . Well, I'm sort of a Sunday writer . . . What I really am is a guy in the sash and door business who got lucky with a book.

HACKETT

What business?

JACK

Sash and door.

SCHATZIE

Shatzendoor?

(TED *shrugs*)

JACK

A couple of years ago things got slow on account of the competition from aluminum. Now all our stuff's all ponderosa pine. (SCHATZIE *and* TED *nod gravely and then look at each other, puzzled*) Well, I had a lot of time on my hands and I got to thinking about the stories Uncle Orville used to tell me.

HACKETT
(*To* SNOW)
I told you there really was such a person.

20

JACK

Oh, there sure was. He was my great-uncle . . . wonderful guy. He was sort of a poetic misfit. Had a lobe missing from his left ear. You remember in the book where he gets drunk and falls in the drawbridge machinery.

TED

That was one of the funniest scenes in the book.

HACKETT

Your dialogue is damned good.

JACK

Well, thanks.

TED

(*A chance to get in*)

I am very high on your dialogue. It has a — a — a roundness. There's . . . there's a three-dimensional thing here, I think.

JACK

Uh-huh.

TED

I feel body, consistency . . . sort of a thickness.

JACK

He makes it sound sort of like fudge.

HACKETT

That's exactly what it sounded like to me, Ted.

21

TED

Dick, what I mean is . . . it's perfect for musical comedy.

JACK

(*He can't believe his ears*)

Musical . . . you mean this is going to be a musical show?

SCHATZIE

What else?

JACK

That's the craziest thing I ever heard of.

HACKETT

I assumed you knew.

(*He turns to look at* TED *accusingly*)

TED

I assumed he knew.

JACK

Well, *I* didn't assume I knew. I thought this was going to be a play. That's the craziest thing I ever heard of. I never wrote a musical comedy.

HACKETT

You never wrote a play, either.

JACK

Well, I can *think* about writing a play. But a musical . . . Who's going to write the songs?

TED
(*Beaming*)

Aaah.

SCHATZIE

Wait'll you hear. You'll flip.

JACK

Who is it?

TED
(*Smugly, to* HACKETT)
Do you want to tell him, Dick, or shall I?

HACKETT

You tell him.

TED
(*Confidentially*)
Jordan, I don't want this to get around, because the deal isn't set yet. But we are in the process of signing up Rudy Lorraine.

SCHATZIE
(*Same tone*)

Rudy Lorraine!

JACK
(*Just repeating the name*)
Rudy Lorraine.

TED
(*Confirming*)
Rudy Lorraine.

JACK
(*He never heard of him*)
Rudy Lorraine??

TED
And please, Jordan, I can't put it too strongly about keeping it quiet. This'll be big news because it's Rudy's first show . . . Well . . . (*Confidentially*) . . . I don't have to tell you about Rudy Lorraine.

JACK
Well, you might tell me something . . . like who the hell is he?

TED
(*Suddenly annoyed*)
Aw, come on, Jordan. You may be from Iowa, but you don't live in a tree.
(*Sits*)

SCHATZIE
(*Excitedly counting up on his fingers, which he practically thrusts in* JACK's *face*)
"Rock Me Papa" . . .

JACK
I beg your pardon?

SCHATZIE
"Adios, Sweetheart, Adios" . . . "Chief of Love" . . . You mean to tell me you never heard of "Chief of Love"?

TED
For four weeks, it's been number one on the jukebox.

24

SAY, DARLING

JACK

I haven't got a jukebox.

SCHATZIE

(*Starting for the record player*)
This is the biggest thing in the country today. Listen to this.

HACKETT

(*He's heard this before*)
Not too loud, Schatzie.

(SCHATZIE *starts the record. He loves the number and dances as it plays.* JACK *hates it but he's trying not to show his hatred too openly.* TED *is nervously watching* JACK's *reaction and trying to look approving.* HACKETT *is looking at his watch*)

Oh my chief of love,
You're my thief of love,
You left me so blue
Crying boo hoo boo hoo hoo hoo
Boo hoo hoo hoo hoo hoo hoo hoo.

Chief of love, sitting in your teepee,
Chief of love, sitting in your teepee,
Why did you leave your squaw so sad and weepy?
You've gone and strayed off the reservation,
You've gone and played off the reservation,
You broke the law of fair game conservation.
Love me only,
Your poor papoose is crying,
I'm so lonely
While on the loose you're flying.
Chief of love, with your eagle feather,
Chief of love, we belong together.

25

Oh please don't be an Indian giver,
Bring your arrows back to my quiver,
Come back home and I will deliver
Love, love, love, love,
You're my chief of love.

SCHATZIE

Well, what do you think?

HACKETT

Frightening, isn't it?

TED

Now wait, Dick, let me explain something to Jordan. (*To* JACK) You understand, this number doesn't in any way represent what we have in mind for our show. But there is big, basic talent there. The man has a drive . . . a raw, untamed power.

JACK

Couldn't we get somebody more like Victor Herbert?

TED

Victor Herbert?

JACK

Yeah, you know. (*Sings*) "Toyland, Toyland."

HACKETT
(*A lecture*)

Jordan, in addition to its glamor, the theater has a vulgar commercial side. Now the public has taken this Rudy Lorraine to its heaving bosom. And Mr. Snow has assured me that Mr. Lorraine will cause a veritable stampede at the box office.

26

TED

And, Dick, in addition to that, he'll write us a good score. Not just a lot of black notes, either. Big hits.

SCHATZIE

Oh, those hit tunes. What they do for you. (*Like an announcer*) And now we present Dinah Shore singing the title song from that new Broadway smash, *The Girl from Indiana.*

JACK

What's that?

SCHATZIE

What's what?

JACK

The Girl from Indiana.

SCHATZIE

That's your title.

TED

(*Carefully*)

You see, Jordan, a title is terribly important in musical comedy and I didn't feel — or rather, we didn't feel that your title, *Paddlewheel,* was quite right. So we decided on a new one.

JACK

The Girl from Indiana. (*Turns to* HACKETT) Mr. Hackett, do you like that?

27

HACKETT

I thought of it. *The Girl from Indiana.* That's good. Indiana is a beautiful word.

SCHATZIE

So is girl.

JACK

But, Mr. Hackett! What's Indiana got to do with anything? My book is about the Chippewa River. It's all laid in Wisconsin.

HACKETT

I've planned to change the river to the Wabash.

JACK

If you fellows wanted to do a show about Indiana, how come you bought a book about Wisconsin?

HACKETT

(*Suddenly, looking at his watch and becoming very snappish*)
Mr. Jordan, we're going to have to change a few things. You have not written the Dead Sea Scrolls.

JACK

Oh, I understand that, but . . .

HACKETT

Musical comedy is my business. You'll have to trust me.

JACK

Oh, I do, Mr. Hackett.

28

HACKETT

Now, I have prepared a rough outline of how I think the first
act should go. We'll stick fairly close to your story line, except
we will open with a husking bee.

JACK

A husking bee! There's no husking bee in my book.

HACKETT
(*Crisply*)

A husking bee will make a very colorful opening. Now I would
like you to have something ready for me by Tuesday.

SCHATZIE

I want to get started on some stuff with you, too — some inter-
views. Jordan, can you go on with Dave Garroway next Wednesday at five-forty-five A.M. in the morning?

JACK

Tuesday? Wednesday? I'll be in Council Falls. I have to be
back at work.

HACKETT

Back at work at what?

JACK

The sash and door business.

SCHATZIE

What the hell is a shatzendoor?

29

JACK

I only took three days off and I've got to get back.

TED

(*Excited and angry*)

Now look, Jordan, we're in a jam, and you can't . . .

HACKETT

Just a minute, Ted. (*To* JACK) Jordan, exactly where and when were you planning to write this show?

JACK

I figured I'd do it the same way I wrote the book — in my spare time. I've got a little shack down by the river where I like to work . . .

HACKETT

Mr. Jordan, you cannot write a Broadway show in your spare time in a shack down by the river. We have to work together, and we have to work fast. If you're going to do this show, you're going to have to forget about everything else. You cannot go back to Council Falls. You have to start working immediately. Today . . . right now . . . right after I've finished my squash game.

JACK

(*Uneasily*)

How long will all this take?

HACKETT

Good God, this is a show. A whole show. You've got to live with us, boy.

JACK

All right. I guess I can take a month off.

TED

A month off! Are you out of your mind? It'll be *six* months, if we're lucky.

SCHATZIE

If this show is a hit, you'll never have to look at another shatzendoor again.

JACK

What about my wife and kids? I got four kids and I'm nuts about them. And I've got a good-looking wife, and if you think I'm going to hang around this town for six months while my family is out in Iowa, you're talking to the wrong Jordan.

HACKETT
(*Sighs*)

Unh. Family man. Well, let's bring the family East.

JACK

Wait a minute.

HACKETT
(*Ignoring him*)

Ted, find Jordan a house. Jordan, where would you like to live?

JACK

In Council Falls, Iowa.

HACKETT
(*Dismissing him*)
You'd better leave it to us.

SCHATZIE
What about some place in Westport?

HACKETT
There's too much drinking up there.

JACK
(*Desperately*)
Look, Mr. Hackett . . .

HACKETT
What about New Rochelle? Don't people live in New Rochelle?
(JACK *is looking wildly from one to the other. They ignore him*)

TED
I think he ought to be closer to you, Dick — say, Stamford.
He'd like it up there.

JACK
What are we going to live on?

HACKETT
We'll arrange an advance. Stamford isn't a bad idea, Ted.

TED
I can get them Bill Richardson's house. It's a wonderful place
for a married couple, and it's available because the Richardsons
just split up.

32

HACKETT

Good!
(JACK *looks sick, clutches his diaphragm. He slumps in a chair*)

JACK

Oh, my God.

TED

What's the matter with you?

JACK

I don't know. I don't know what to think. Stamford. Six months. "Chief of Love."

HACKETT

That's all right. You're just excited. You'll feel better once you start working.

JACK
(*Suddenly leaping up*)
NO, NO, NO, NO, NO. I'm not going to do it.

TED

Jordan. Wait.

JACK
(*Going on*)
No Stamford. No *Girl from Indiana*. No husking bee.

TED

Now, Jordan, I'm sure . . .

33

JACK

I'm no great writer. I wrote one little book. But I like it. And if you want to mess it all up, then get yourself somebody who doesn't care. Husking bee! I hate husking bees.

TED

Now, Jordan. I'm sure Dick isn't married to the husking bee.

JACK

It's not just that.

HACKETT

Jordan, I want you to understand one thing. I respect your integrity as an author. I would no more force you to do something against your will . . .
(*Door opens; we hear* JUNE's *voice, off stage*)

JUNE'S VOICE

They're having a meeting, Miss Lovelle.

IRENE

(*Entering*)

I love meetings.
(HACKETT *stops talking, in annoyance*)

SCHATZIE

Hi, Irene.

IRENE

Hi, Schatzie darling. (*To others*) Am I interrupting something important?

HACKETT

Yes, you are, dear.

IRENE

Good. You'll have to be real sweet if you want to get rid of me.

TED

Irene, I thought we were going to meet at Sardi's.

IRENE

I was early so I thought I'd pick you up. (*To* HACKETT) Besides, Dick, I thought it wouldn't hurt to come in and dazzle you a bit so that you'd keep me in mind.

HACKETT

Keep you in mind for what?
(IRENE *looks at* TED)

TED

Dick, I've been meaning to discuss this with you. Irene has read the book and she's very much interested in the girl's part.

IRENE

You're a big help. "Interested in the girl's part"! I want that part, and I'm going to get it. And I'll shoot anybody that gets in my way.

HACKETT

It's too soon to talk about that.

35

IRENE

It can't be too soon. What do you think I'm hanging around New York for? I've turned down fifty movie offers. Hollywood, Italy, Spain, the Belgian Congo.

HACKETT

Belgian Congo?

IRENE

I want to do a show, and, boy, what a show this *Paddlewheel* is going to make. You guys really have something there.

HACKETT

I agree with you, Irene . . .

IRENE

(*Interrupting*)

Another thing I like is the show takes place in 1895. My numerologist told me that twenty-four was my lucky combination number, and one-eight-nine-five adds up to twenty-four, and I want the part.

HACKETT

Wait a minute, Irene. It adds up to twenty-three.

IRENE

I still want the part.

TED

Oh, I'm sorry. Irene, this is Jack Jordan. Jack, this is Irene Lovelle.

JACK

You don't have to tell me who she is. This is a great pleasure,
Miss Lovelle. I've seen you in so many movies . . .

IRENE

Jack Jordan . . . You wrote *Paddlewheel.*

TED

That's right. Now we hope he's going to write our show.

IRENE

I'm a big fan of yours. I'm mad about your book.

JACK

You're very kind, Miss Lovelle.

IRENE

You know, I swore to myself that if I ever met the man who
wrote that beautiful book, I was going to fall madly in love with
him. You're wonderful.
(*She embraces him*)

JACK

Gee, I was only going to ask you for your autograph.

IRENE

(*To* TED *and* HACKETT)
You see, he's just as witty as he was in the book.

TED

We think so.

IRENE

Ted, let's take him to lunch with us.

TED

(*Leaping into action*)

Grand idea.

HACKETT

Splendid.

TED

Irene, why don't you and Jordan run over to Sardi's and get a table. I'll be there in a minute.

IRENE

Fine.

TED

You'll love Sardi's, Jordan, and we can have a good long talk.

JACK

Well, I don't know if I should or not. You see I . . .

IRENE

(*Taking* JACK'S *arm*)

Come along . . . Jack.

JACK

Okay . . . Irene.

(*They go*)

FAST DIM

Scene Three

Breakfast room in Stamford.
We hear television noises. As stage lights up, we see Jack
at the breakfast table, writing on a yellow legal pad. He
stops.

JACK
(*Shouting stage right*)
Johnny, turn that thing down.

FRANKIE
(*Entering carrying a pot of coffee*)
Do what your father said.
(*Television goes off*)

JACK
It didn't take him long to find that television set.

FRANKIE
It fascinates him. Back home we only have one channel. Here
he has an embarrassment of riches.

JACK
Well, I'm trying to get some work done. Where are the rest
of the bandits?

FRANKIE

Billy and the twins are out in front, making insulting remarks about the state of Connecticut.

JACK

Well, they'll get used to it.

FRANKIE

I guess they will, and I guess I will, too.

JACK

I know you will, Frankie. I've been here in the East only three weeks, and I never want to go back to Council Falls.

FRANKIE

Never?

JACK

Oh, I couldn't stand it. Spending every other night with Archie and Helen, and you don't like Helen. Having lunch every day with Old Man Johnson, the sole topic of conversation is should we or should we not get a new sawdust burner. And that witty repartee. "Where you going, Jack?"

FRANKIE

"New York."

JACK

"New York. What are you going there for?"

FRANKIE

"It's about this book I wrote."

40

JACK

"Oh, yeah, you did write a book. Funny —"

JACK AND FRANKIE

"I never did get to read that book."

JACK

Honey, these people in show business — they may be hard to work with, they may be unpredictable, but they're sure exciting to be with. And one other thing, Frankie — they've all read my book.

(*He lights a cigarette*)

FRANKIE

When did you start smoking tailor-made cigarettes?

JACK

Oh, honey, you can't go around New York City rolling your own. That's corny. I got to get this stuff into town.

FRANKIE

You leaving?

JACK

I hate to do this to you on your first day, but Hackett wants this stuff right away.

FRANKIE

You never used to work Saturdays.

41

JACK

Honey, you don't understand. Saturdays off? That's for civilians. We glamorous, gossamer show folks work all the time. Today we got a big meeting with Rudy Lorraine. He's going to play us the first song he's written for the show.

FRANKIE

I hope it's nothing like "Chief of Love."
(*She sings a couple of lines from song*)

JACK

All right, wise guy. Kid it all you like, but it's still in the top ten.

FRANKIE

But you told me yourself it made you carsick.

JACK

Wait till you see Rudy Lorraine. He's one of those smart, tough guys who can do anything. Why, I was having lunch with Irene Lovelle the other day and she says he's . . .

FRANKIE

Irene Lovelle? Do you know her?

JACK

Know her? She may play a part in my show. Irene's a singer who really knows her business and you should hear her talk about Rudy.

FRANKIE

What's she like?

JACK

Irene? Wonderful girl, Frankie. And really built. (*He stops*) Oh, she's just an actress. Talks all the time.

FRANKIE

Did you two have lunch alone?

JACK

Oh, no. Sardi's is always crowded. This was strictly business. She wanted the author's interpretation of the role. I've got to finish dressing.

FRANKIE

Funny thing. I can't imagine what part she would want.

JACK

Irene? She wants to play Rosie.

FRANKIE

Rosie was a brunette. She was a Chippewa girl.

JACK

Well, there have been some changes. Now she's Italian.
(*He goes off, returns*)

FRANKIE

Italian? Rosie Runningdeer is an Italian?

JACK

We've changed her name to Rosie Rizzuto. (FRANKIE *looks at him blankly*) You remember that part in the book about the carnival and the Italian girl.

43

FRANKIE

But Uncle Orville never met her in the book.

JACK

Well, now he does meet her, and falls in love with her. You see, the show opens when Rosie comes to a party on the boat.

FRANKIE

A party on Uncle Orville's boat?

JACK

Look, I'm lucky. At least it's on the boat. Hackett wanted to open with a husking bee. I talked him out of that. A party won't be so bad, Frankie. This is musical comedy.

FRANKIE

Hold it a minute. Never mind musical comedy. What about you? Jack Jordan?

JACK
(*Defensive*)

What about me?

FRANKIE

These changes . . . all this stuff you're doing . . . Are you happy about it?

JACK
(*Flaring up*)

Sure I'm happy. What difference does it make? Why in hell do I have to be happy all the time? (*Puts his arms around her, gives a sigh of relief*) Frankie, I'm glad you're here. I haven't had anybody to holler at for a month.

44

FRANKIE

I figured that. That's the only reason I didn't slug you.

(*During the above,* JACK *has been putting on tie and jacket — is now dressed to go out*)

JACK

(*Looks at his watch*)

Hey, I only got a few minutes. Frankie, you get organized here. And make those kids help you.

(*He kisses her on the cheek, starts off. She grabs his coat-tail*)

FRANKIE

Just one thing I still can't understand.

JACK

What?

FRANKIE

If Rosie is an Italian girl, how can a redhead like Irene Lovelle get the part?

JACK

Easy. By sleeping with the author.

(*He smacks her on the behind and exits*)

BLACKOUT

45

Scene Four

The producers' office.
The secretary, June, stands at the desk. Schatzie is on
stage. Phone rings. June answers phone.

JUNE

Hello. No, Mr. Jordan isn't here just now. Who's calling? (*Suddenly very friendly*) Oh, hello, Mrs. Jordan. How are you? I'm June, the secretary. We're all dying to meet you. Have a nice trip? Good. What? Mr. Jordan *was* here but he went out for a drink with Miss Lovelle. Irene Lovelle. Shall I have him call you when he gets back? All right. I'll just tell him you called. 'By now, dear. (TED *enters, carrying a folded newspaper, looking at it*) Hope to see you soon.

(*Hangs up*)

TED
(*Going to* SCHATZIE)

Say, Schatzie . . .

JUNE

That was Mrs. Jordan on the phone, looking for Mr. Jordan. She sounds like a lovely person.

TED

He'll be here in a few minutes.

46

JUNE

Oh, he's here. I mean, he was here. He and Miss Lovelle just stepped out for a drink.

TED

Miss Lovelle? Was she here?

JUNE

Yes. She came in here looking for you.

SCHATZIE

But she found Jack Jordan instead. I'd say she was really working on him.

TED

That will be all, June. (JUNE *leaves*) I think Irene's been working on you, too. (*Holding out newspaper*) Schatzie, did you plant this item?

SCHATZIE

(*Looking at paper — reads*)
"American satellite still in orbit." I didn't plant that.

TED

You know what item I mean. (*Reads*) "Irene Lovelle top contender for lead in *Girl from Indiana.*"

SCHATZIE

Well, it was a little quiet around here and I saw a chance to steal a little space.

47

TED

This is extremely awkward, Schatzie. Very embarrassing.

SCHATZIE

Why? She's going to get the part eventually, ain't she?

TED

I'm not at all sure of that.

SCHATZIE

Well, this is an interesting switch.

TED

What's an interesting switch?

SCHATZIE

Most producers are fighting to get their broads into shows.

TED

Schatzie, I don't like that word.

SCHATZIE

What word? Producers?

TED

Just because I've had a few dates with Irene doesn't mean that
I would use my influence . . . to get her into a show . . .
(HACKETT *enters from inner office*)

HACKETT

What's all this?

48

TED

Did you see this item Schatzie planted?

HACKETT

Yes. It's a little premature, but it's publicity. And besides, the more I think about Irene, the more I like her for the part.

TED

Let's go slow on this, Dick. We haven't consulted Rudy Lorraine at all yet. An item like this is liable to upset him. You know, Rudy's pretty sensitive.

HACKETT

Sensitive? Any man who could write "Chief of Love" hasn't a nerve in his body.

TED

Dick, I don't like your attitude towards Rudy. You know this is the first time he's going to be coming in here and playing the new stuff.

HACKETT

All right, all right. We'll consult him. But he should be glad to get Irene. She looks good, has talent, she's a Name. And besides, she needs a show, so she won't cost us much.

TED

Well, Dick, I had hoped that, casting-wise, we could go for the bolder stroke. A big voice! Somebody with the grandeur and elegance of the grand opera!

HACKETT

The grand opera?!

TED

It's been done. Think of the news value if we could say, *The Girl from Indiana,* starring Maria Callas. Well, I mean I hardly think —

HACKETT

You hardly think. That's a pretty good description of you, Ted. Look, I should think *you'd* be particularly happy to have Irene in the show.

TED

Now that's what I'm trying to avoid, Dick. I don't want people to think that just because I've been running around with Irene, I have forced her on my associates.

HACKETT

Wait a minute, Ted. I don't think an actress should get a part because she's the producer's girl. But I don't think she should lose it for that reason, either. If it will make you feel any better, I used to run around with Irene, myself. If Irene is right for the part . . . (JUNE *enters*) . . . we're going to use her.

JUNE
(*Excited*)

It's Mr. Lorraine.

RUDY
(*Entering*)

Hi, fellows.

50

SCHATZIE

Hi, Rudy.

TED

Good to see you, Rudy.

HACKETT

Hello.

RUDY

(*To* JUNE)

Look, sweetie, I'm expecting a call from a young lady.

JUNE

I'll put the call in here.

RUDY

No, we'll be working. Just give her a message. Tell her six o'clock at my place.

JUNE

Okay.

(*She goes*)

RUDY

(*Going to piano*)

Well, fellows, Rudy Lorraine has brought you a case full of goodies. Got a great song for Rosie here. Boy, we're going to need somebody good to play her.

TED

We're going to get somebody good, Rudy.

RUDY

Hey, did you guys see that crazy item in the paper about Irene Lovelle doing Rosie? That was funny. Did you guys plant this item?

TED

It was a mistake, Rudy.

SCHATZIE

It was my fault, Rudy. I goofed. I'm terribly overworked.

HACKETT

It was a little premature.

RUDY

Hey! You guys aren't really thinking of Irene for the part of Rosie?

HACKETT

She's a strong possibility. Don't judge her by her movies. Irene's fine on the stage.

RUDY

Now wait a minute! If I give this show the benefit of my name, I have every right to expect a star with just as big a reputation as mine.

HACKETT

Reputation for what?

TED

Rudy, Irene is just one of many people we're considering . . .

52

RUDY

This part of Rosie calls for a big, big star. A dame who can really belt a song.

HACKETT

Mr. Lorraine, big stars don't care to risk their reputations with the music of an unknown song writer.

RUDY

Unknown! Me, unknown? Who doesn't know Rudy Lorraine?

HACKETT

Offhand, I can think of nine people, and they're all critics. You see, Rudy, someone like Irene Lovelle would be very eager to . . .

RUDY

I don't want Irene Lovelle. (*Turns to* TED) And let me tell you, Ted, you're not going to get her into this show just because you're playing house with her.

TED

I think that's terribly unfair, Rudy. First of all, I've only been seeing Irene once in a while, and . . .

HACKETT

Never mind that, Ted. Look, Rudy, why all this volcanic reaction to Irene? Have you worked with her before?

RUDY

Worked with her? I used to be married to her.

HACKETT
(*Understanding*)

Oooh.

RUDY

It was a long time ago, in Hollywood, when I used to play piano for her.

HACKETT

I see, and you don't care to do a show with an ex-wife.

RUDY

That's not it at all.

HACKETT

Well, suppose we auditioned Irene, and you liked her . . .

RUDY

Look, I'm the composer. I write the songs. I pick the singers. I'm not here to rebuild Irene Lovelle's career. I'm in the Rudy Lorraine business. Well, let's get to work.

HACKETT

This may be the first show in history to give program credit to a staff psychiatrist.

RUDY

Are you ready to hear a real show stopper?

HACKETT

Guaranteed?

RUDY

What do you mean by that?

TED

(*Leaping in*)
Rudy, I think what Dick means is that on Broadway, there is
no certainty.

RUDY

(*Patiently*)
Look, I know songs. And I know people. I'm in the people business. I know how to give people what they want. I don't care
whether it's jukeboxes, radio, TV, or Broadway. It's still people.

TED

Well, Rudy, on Broadway there is a difference in climate and
level of audience.

RUDY

Please — What's an audience? People. Who's going to be there
opening night? People . . . human beings.

HACKETT

Let's just say "people." (*Looking at his watch*) Ted, let's get
on with this.

TED

We have to wait for Jack.
(RUDY *goes to piano, sits down and strikes a chord. The
door opens and* TWO BOP MUSICIANS, *wearing berets and
beards, look in*)

MUSICIAN

You ready for us, man?

RUDY

Not yet, boys. Stick around.

MUSICIAN

Okay, Daddio.

(*They go*)

HACKETT
(*Stunned*)

What was that?

RUDY

A couple of sidemen. They're going to play with me.

HACKETT

They are?

RUDY

Sure. Man, I want you to dig this stuff right.
(*He goes to noodling at the piano.* HACKETT *looks at him, shaking his head*)

TED

Hey, Rudy. What's that you're playing?

RUDY

That's one of my old songs.

SAY, DARLING

JACK
(*Entering with* IRENE)
Since he shot the Justice of the Peace, nobody will talk to him.
(*To* TED) I'm sorry I'm late.

IRENE
(*Cutting in*)
Ted, it's all my fault. I made Mr. Jordan buy me another . . .
(*She stops as she becomes aware of the piano and who is playing it*)

TED
Really, Irene, we've kept our composer waiting . . .
(IRENE *sees* RUDY. *They look at each other*)

IRENE
(*Very friendly*)
Hello, Rudy.

RUDY
(*Casually*)
Hi, Irene.

JACK
Isn't Irene wonderful? She knows everybody.

SCHATZIE
A very friendly person.
(IRENE *starts singing rhythmically*)

IRENE

Try to love me just as I am.
Try to understand
That I can be much more than I am,
If you'll hold my hand.

For it makes you grow to know
You're loved for what you are;
So just the way I am
Please say you'll take me.
Then I can climb as high as the sky,
Your love will help me try.

(*Turns to others*)
It's always been my favorite song of Rudy's. (*To* RUDY) Rudy, I
still think it's a great song.

RUDY

I still think it's a dog. I never could give it away, and you never
could pick them.

IRENE
(*Sighs*)
No . . . I guess I couldn't.

RUDY
(*Stops playing, breaks mood*)
Well, Irene, thanks for the audition. We've got to get to work.

IRENE
(*After a stunned pause, talking through her teeth*)
I was not auditioning, buddy boy. When I do, you will know
it.

TED

(*Rises*)

Irene, please, uh . . .

IRENE

Look, Ted, I'm sorry I broke in on your meeting, but I wanted to tell you how thrilled I was about that item in the paper.

JACK

Irene and I just had a drink to celebrate. I think she'll make a great Rosie.

RUDY

Don't believe everything you read in the papers.

TED

Irene, it's just that the item was a little premature.

IRENE

You mean it isn't true?

TED

Not exactly.

IRENE

Now look, Ted, I won't be brushed off on this show. I want this part. Rudy, you know I can do this girl great.

RUDY

I don't know. Maybe you've been singing with microphones too long. Maybe they can't hear you in a theater.

59

IRENE

Okay, okay. Tell you what. I don't usually do auditions. I don't have to. But for this part, I will. When do you want to hear me?

TED

Well, it's, uh . . .

IRENE

Yes?

TED

It's up to Dick.

IRENE

(*Turning to* HACKETT *and addressing him in a business-like tone*)
I'm ready whenever you want to hear me, Dick.

HACKETT

Fine, Irene.

RUDY

(*Cutting in*)
Just a minute. We're not ready to hear anybody yet. I've just started the score. Besides I don't know what kind of a dame I want to sing this part. I'm not sure if . . .

IRENE

Oh, shut up . . . Up . . . Shut . . . Up! I'm sick of this whole cotton-picking project. I want no part of it.

JACK

Now, Irene, don't get yourself all upset . . .

IRENE

You shut up, too. I've had it. It's too much.

TED

Now listen, Irene.

IRENE

Aw, go back to Princeton. Good-by.

HACKETT
(*Calmly*)

Say, Irene.

IRENE
(*Angrily*)

What do you want?

HACKETT

About the audition. How about Thursday, at two?

IRENE

I'll *be* there.

(*She goes out*)

RUDY

Now what the hell is going on around here? I told you how I felt.

HACKETT

I think Irene deserves a hearing.

RUDY

I don't want that tomato in this show.

JACK

I don't like to hear that kind of talk about a lady.

RUDY

Lady? She's a singer.

JACK

Well, I think she's a lady, and a singer (JUNE *enters*), and a fine singer, too.

JUNE

Excuse me, Mr. Jordan, I forgot to tell you — your wife called a while ago and I told her you were out with Miss Lovelle.

JACK

That was real neighborly of you. Did she want me to call her?

JUNE

No.

(JUNE *goes*)

HACKETT
(*Looking at his watch*)

Look, I'm playing squash at five o'clock. Come on, Rudy, and let's hear what you've got.

RUDY

Okay. (*He goes to the door and calls off*) Let's go, boys.
(*He goes back to the piano*)

JACK

Say, if you don't mind, I think I'll just give my wife a call.

RUDY

Oh, for God's sake.

HACKETT

Come on, family man. (*The* TWO MUSICIANS *enter, carrying a
bass and guitar. They get set next to the piano*) We've got to
work. (JACK *sits down*) Go ahead, Rudy.
(RUDY *is at the piano*)

RUDY

Of course, you haven't given me much to go on. There's only
half a script.

HACKETT

Rudy — Jack's been working very hard.

TED

That's the way good shows are done, Rudy — the songs and
the book at the same time. That's the way Rodgers and Hammerstein work.

RUDY

(*Under his breath, contemptuously*)

Rodgers and Hammerstein. (*Noodles some more*) Now here's
the opening number that Rosie sings to Orville when she's try-

ing to get him to give up his steamboat and leave the river. I just ad-libbed some rough dialogue to lead into it. Rosie says, "Listen Orville — your number is up. You've been working these riverboats for years. But you're heading for an accident — disaster." Then Orville says, "How do you know?" And she says, "I am a famous fortuneteller."

> I know what a person's gonna do before he does it.
> I know what a person's gonna say before he says it.
> I know what's gonna happen to a person before it happens,
> From looking into my crystal ball.
> Oooo-ee heerinnay a hara babab canbi rama
> Kay gay innay aha!
> Ah! ha!

And then Orville says, "What's gonna happen to me, Rosie?" And Rosie says:

> It's doom, it's doom.
> It's absolutely positively doom.
> This is the zero hour.
> It's up to you,
> It lies within your power.
> Whatcha gonna do, whatcha gonna do, gonna do?
> Fate, it's fate.
> You've got to act before it's too late.
> While you still have a chance,
> Get up, get up and go.
> How do I know, how do I know?
> The crystal ball just told me.
> Aha!
> I know what a person's gonna do before he does it.
> I know what a person's gonna say before he says it.
> I know what's gonna happen to a person before it happens.
> Whatcha gonna do, whatcha gonna do, gonna do?
> Fate, it's fate.

You've got to act before it's too late.
Come on, get off the ship,
Make this your final trip,
And you'll escape the grip of doom, doom, doom, doom, doom!
Doom!

SCHATZIE

(*Leaping up with great enthusiasm*)
Great Rudy, just great! (*To* TED) Ted, that's really got it.

TED

(*Very carefully*)
I thought it was quite interesting. Had some good things in it.
Don't you think so, Jack?

JACK

I thought it was a nice song. Real nice.

TED

What did you think of it, Dick?

HACKETT

(*Gives* TED *a long look, turns to* RUDY)
What else have you got, Rudy?

RUDY

Take five, boys. (MUSICIANS *exit*) (*Turning to* HACKETT) So
you didn't like that number, huh?

HACKETT

Frankly, no. I think it's wrong.

65

RUDY
(*Half puzzled, half angry*)

Wrong??

TED

What Dick means, Rudy, is that it has the . . . the wrong texture for the fabric of our show.

RUDY
(*Exploding*)

I don't know what the hell you're talking about, and I don't think you do, either. I think it's a damn good song and I'm the only one here qualified to judge it.

TED

Now, Rudy . . .

RUDY
(*Going on*)

Texture . . . Fabric . . . What is this, cloaks and suits? I'm in the music business.

HACKETT

A minute ago you were in the people business.

RUDY

All right, Mr. Hackett. Just tell me one thing that's wrong with this song. One legitimate thing.

HACKETT

It doesn't fit. Jack, do you see any possible way of fitting this song in our story?

66

JACK
(*Hesitantly*)
Well . . . of course, Rosie isn't a fortuneteller.

RUDY
(*Hollers*)
Well, she *could* be, damn it.

HACKETT
Well, she's not. And if she were, I think you have made her sound like the most repulsive fortuneteller in the history of the occult.

RUDY
You think! Well, maybe what you think isn't as important as what you think it is.

TED
Now, Rudy, remember this is *the* Richard Hackett who has been responsible for over twenty musical shows on Broadway.

RUDY
(*Contemptuously*)
Yeah? Well, I saw his last show. I'm one of the *few* people who saw it. Schatzie liked the song. Schatzie, didn't you like the song?

SCHATZIE
What song?

RUDY
(*Points to* HACKETT)
You're just scared of him.

67

HACKETT

Mr. Lorraine, I was warned that you have more talent than breeding. Let's get one thing straight. I don't care how you feel about me just so long as you remember that I am running this show. If you don't like that, you can eliminate yourself. And you can feel free to translate that into more colorful terms.

(HACKETT *exits*)

TED

Now, Rudy, what Dick means is . . .

RUDY

I don't care what he means, I'm through. I've had it.

(RUDY *goes out*, TED *and* SCHATZIE *following*)

TED

Now, Rudy, wait . . .

SCHATZIE

Wait a minute, fellows.

(*They go*)

JACK

(*Picks up phone*)

Operator, Stamford, Connecticut, please. Davis five two seven five oh. This is Plaza three six seven four oh. (*Sings*) "Doom, it's doom . . ." Hello, Frankie? Sorry I couldn't call you back sooner, but this place has been a madhouse. What? Frankie, I was not out getting drunk with Irene Lovelle. I had two little double Martinis. Look, we got worse troubles. That crazy Rudy Lorraine just up and quit the show. This whole project is blowing up. And it may be a good thing, too. (HACKETT *re-enters from his office. He has some papers with him*) I think you'd better stop unpacking.

HACKETT

Say, Jack . . .

JACK

Excuse me, honey. Will you hold on for a minute? (*Puts down phone. Then to* HACKETT) I was just giving my wife the bad news.

HACKETT
(*Ignoring the remark*)
I have a pretty good layout here for the fourth and fifth scenes. I'd like a rough draft on this as fast as you can get it done. This may be the key to the show.

JACK
(*Stunned*)
Is there going to be a show? I mean, Rudy just quit. It looked to me as if everybody was . . .
(RUDY, *followed by* TED, *and the* SIDEMEN *re-enter*)

RUDY
No, Ted, no — nobody talks to Rudy Lorraine that way.

TED
Rudy, if you'll just listen.

RUDY

I can't see what's wrong with this song. (*Begins his chant*)
Aha!

HACKETT

(*Sharply*)

Now you stop that. (RUDY *stops*) I told you that song is out.

RUDY

Damn it! This is an opening number. Do you think it's easy to
find ideas for opening numbers?

HACKETT

Well, first of all, I don't think the show should open on the
boat.

RUDY

Well, that's where the script opens. I tried to make it fit.

HACKETT

That's because of Mr. Jordan's wishes. I've always felt the
show should open at a husking bee.

RUDY

(*Thinking*)

Husking bee . . .

JACK

Now, Mr. Hackett, you promised me that . . .

HACKETT

I know, I know.

70

RUDY

(*Liking the idea more*)

Husking bee. Hey, I could do a hoedown, country-style. The kind of stuff I used to write for Tennessee Ernie. Vamp about here, Charlie — key of C. Very commercial.

(*The* MUSICIAN *begins playing chords with a country beat and* RUDY *sings the words "Husking bee, husking bee, meet me at the husking bee."* PETER *joins him. They keep the rhythmic thing going. Everybody else is smiling and bouncing with the rhythm*)

HACKETT

That's very good!

JACK

Now wait a minute, everybody. It was distinctly understood . . .

HACKETT

Wait a minute. This sounds good!

JACK

You told me that my novel would not be interfered with.

HACKETT

Jack, if it's no good we can always take it out.

RUDY

(*Sings, during this*)

"The corn is green, the sky is blue. The first prize is a kiss from you. The husking bee, the husking bee. Meet me at the husking bee."

71

(JACK *backs away in horror, suddenly remembers* FRANKIE *on phone*)

JACK

Frankie! I forgot about Frankie. (*Runs to phone*) Hello, Frankie. I'm sorry I made you wait so long. I can't talk to you now, honey. They're playing the husking bee number. Yes, husking bee. I know, Frankie, I know. But this is musical comedy. Dammit, Frankie, a husking bee will make a very colorful opening.

RUDY
(*Singing*)
The corn is green.

JACK
(*Echoing* RUDY)
The corn is green.

RUDY
The sky is blue.

JACK
The sky is blue.

RUDY AND JACK
First prize is a kiss from you.
The husking bee, the husking bee,
Shuck a little corn at the husking bee.

CURTAIN

ACT TWO

ACT TWO

SCENE ONE

An audition stage. Maurice, the conductor, is vamping at the piano, along with Rudy's sidemen. Rudy is "out front" in the "theater" on stage, looking at a sheet of music. Ted is seated "out front." Schatzie enters, sits. Charlie Williams, the stage manager, enters.

CHARLIE

When do you want to start, Mr. Snow? I've got some people waiting.

RUDY

Charlie, I'm just going to sing a song for Mr. Snow.

CHARLIE

I'm very sorry.

TED

We'll be with you in a minute, Charlie. Mr. Lorraine's going to sing me a new number for the show. Besides, there's no use auditioning anybody until Mr. Hackett gets here. Go on, Rudy.

(CHARLIE *exits*)

RUDY

(*Sings*)

I don't fall for all those pretty stories
That tell the tale of love at first sight,
For it's the second time you meet that matters,
How can you tell in one night?
I don't buy those first enchanted evenings
Or songs that say "It's love at a glance,"
For it's the second time you meet that matters,
Love is no one-shot romance;
But on that first night that I saw you I trembled,
I felt a thrill when you walked in the door,
I waited and then saw you again,
I felt the same thrill, only more.

(HACKETT *enters, stops and listens*)

So never trust that first electric moment,
That magic switch that turns on the heat,
For though you think you've found the one who matters,
You'll never know till the second time you meet —
Until the second time you meet.

(*Spoken*)

Thanks, Maurice.

TED

Very interesting, Rudy, very interesting.

HACKETT

(*Going to* RUDY)

What's that?

RUDY

It's a new number for that spot where Orville first meets Rosie.
I think it's a real gasser. Here, let me do it for you.

76

HACKETT

No, no, you don't have to. I don't like it.

RUDY

How can you tell? You haven't heard it.

HACKETT

I heard "That first electric moment that magic switch turns on the heat." Rudy, this show takes place in eighteen ninety-five.

RUDY

Can't I ever do anything to please you guys?

HACKETT

You've been doing fine, Rudy. Your second act opening has been going through my head all day. It's very good, very good. Save this number for your next show.
(*He goes out front*)

TED

Sorry, Rudy.

RUDY

Do me a favor. Slam the lid on my head.

TED

Come along, boy.
(RUDY *follows him, shaking his head*)

SCHATZIE

Hello, Mr. Hackett.

HACKETT

Hello. What are you doing here, Schatzie? I thought you hated auditions.

SCHATZIE

It's true. I find them extremely painful to the nerves. But I didn't want to miss hearing Irene.

HACKETT
(*To* TED)

Where's Jordan?

TED

Well, I figured he didn't have to hear all these other singers, so he's having lunch with Irene, and he's going to bring her over.

HACKETT

Lunch again? The old family man is branching out a bit. I hope it doesn't slow up his work.

TED

Oh, I think it's quite harmless. Boy from Iowa comes to New York, meets beautiful star — we all have to go through it, Dick. (*Goes to foot of audition stage*) Charlie. Charlie Williams. (CHARLIE *comes on*) Let's go. And let's move it right along. We want to be through with these people before Miss Lovelle gets here.

CHARLIE

Very well, Mr. Snow. (*He walks to the wings and addresses people that we don't see*) Ladies and gentlemen, we are ready

78

to begin our auditions. Now, you may be stopped at any time during your song. If we seem to be interrupting you abruptly, please understand that no criticism or offense is intended. We're just trying to hear as many people as possible and to give everyone a chance. When you have finished, please take your music and leave. We will be in touch with you. Thank you. (*Turns and suddenly shouts in the other direction*) Kill the house lights, Eddie. (*House lights are killed in the theater itself and the lights dimmed in the seating portion of the stage. The stage portion of the stage on stage is lit by the illusion of a work light*) Let's go. (GIRL *enters*) Gentlemen, this is Arlene McKee, soprano.

(ARLENE *walks over to the piano player, hands him her music, goes center stage*)

TED

(*Calls out*)

Will you stand back a little, Miss McKee, under the light, so we can see you.

(ARLENE *moves back, nods to the piano player. He strikes up introduction.* ARLENE *sings*)

ARLENE

I could have danced all night,
I could have danced all night,
And still . . .

TED

(*Calls out*)

Thank you.

(ARLENE *stops, gets her music and goes*)

79

ARLENE

Thank you.

CHARLIE

(*Coming out*)

Miss Jennifer Stevenson, alto.

(JENNIFER *gives her music to pianist, gets into position,
piano starts*)

JENNIFER

I could have danced all night,
I could have . . .

TED

(*Calls*)

Thank you.

(*She takes her music from piano and goes*)

CHARLIE

(*Coming out*)

Mr. Earl Jorgeson.

(EARL *gives music to pianist, etc.*)

EARL

Old Man River, that Old Man River,
He don't . . .

TED

Thank you. (EARL *goes on singing*) Thank you. Thank you very
much.

(EARL *finally stops, gets his music and goes off*)

EARL

Thank you.

SAY, DARLING

CHARLIE

Miss Cheryl Merrill, alto.

CHERYL
(Enters)
If you don't mind, I'd like to do a piece of special material. I
brought my own accompanist.

TED

Fine.

(MAN enters, goes to piano)

CHERYL
(Sings)
Why, why did he leave me,
Why did he leave me alone?
I walk the tortured streets
And my heart is a shrieking stone!
I pass a couple in love,
And my soul is filled with hate.
I shudder at her sweet good-bys
As she whispers to her mate:

I could have danced all night,
I could have danced all . . .

TED, HACKETT, RUDY, SCHATZIE
(Rise, stopping her)

Thank you.

CHERYL

Thank you.

(Gets music, exits with accompanist)

81

SCHATZIE

You're welcome.

RUDY

She almost had me fooled for a minute.

CHARLIE

Gentlemen, Mr. Sammy Miles.
(SAMMY *comes out, gives music to pianist. When the piano starts, he does a fast tap dance*)

TED

Just a minute, just a minute, sir. Whoa. Stop. (SAMMY *stops*) This call is for singers. Are you a singer?

SAMMY

Well, I thought there might be something for a dancer.

TED

Well, there will be dancing, but not tap dancing.

SAMMY

What's the matter with tap dancing?

TED

Nothing, but our choreographer is from the ballet, and his type of choreography calls for . . .

SAMMY

Will you tell me what's the matter with tap dancing?

TED

I'm trying to explain . . .

SAMMY

(*Blowing his top*)

Took me ten years to learn to dance like this. What's wrong with all you Broadway guys? What's the matter with tap dancing? Now nobody wants no tap dancers. Well, that's what I am, a tap dancer.

(*He starts doing a wild tap dance*)

TED

Charlie!

(CHARLIE *comes out, pulls* SAMMY *off stage*)

SAMMY

(*Dancing as he goes*)

That damned Agnes de Mille.

(*He goes*)

TED

What was that?

HACKETT

Poor chap. I know just what he means. You know, Ted, I remember when you couldn't do a show without a couple of dozen tap dancers.

TED

Now, Dick, you surely wouldn't suggest . . .

HACKETT

I guess not. But when I go to shows these days and see all the fluttering, flying and flittering, I sure get lonesome for Buck and Bubbles. Get his name. We may use him for something. Oh, Rudy, I hate to bring this up again, but when Irene sings . . .

(JACK *enters "on stage"*)

RUDY

(*Interrupting*)

I know, I know. I'll be a little gentleman.

JACK

(*Peering over the footlights*)

Hello, fellows. Irene's fixing her face in the dressing room. (JACK *looks up into the flies*) Boy, this is big. This going to be our theater?

HACKETT

No, we're just using it for auditions.

(JACK *is drawn as if by a magnet toward the footlights*)

JACK

(*Recites*)

You'd scarce expect one of my age
To speak in public on the stage,
And if I chance to fall below
Demosthenes or Cicero
Don't view me with a critic's eye
But pass my imperfections by.
Large streams from little fountains flow,
Tall oaks from little acorns grow —

84

TED

Thank you.

HACKETT

That was very good, Mr. Jordan.

RUDY

Mr. Jordan, this is an audition for singers. Have you got a song for us?

JACK

You are looking at the baritone soloist of my church choir. (*To pianist*) Do you know that old hymn "Let the Lower Lights Be Burning"?

MAURICE

What key?

JACK

Oh hell, he does know it. (*Sighs*) Any key.

TED

Will you stand back a little, Mr. Jordan. Under the light so we can see you.

JACK
(*Sings*)
Brightly beams our Father's mercy
From His lighthouse evermore.
But to us He leaves the keeping
Of the lights along the shore.

Let the lower lights be burning,
Send a gleam across the wave,
Some poor fainting, struggling seaman
You may rescue, you may save.

(HACKETT *joins in.* JACK *harmonizes*)

Trim your feeble lamp, my brother.
Some poor seaman, tempest-tossed,
Trying now to make the harbor,
In the darkness may be lost.

Let the lower light be burning,
Send a gleam across the wave . . .

(*Sees* IRENE)

Oh, hi, Irene.

IRENE
(*Entering*)
This is going to be a pretty tough act to follow.

JACK

Good luck, Irene.
(*He goes "out front"*)

IRENE
Thanks. (*She hands music to* MUSICIANS, *who are on stage by now. She goes forward on stage, addresses those in seats*) Hello.
(*They ad-lib "Hellos"*)

HACKETT
What are you going to sing for us, Irene?

IRENE
I'm no fool. I'm going to sing "Chief of Love."

86

HACKETT

Not too loud, Irene.

SCHATZIE

Great!

(IRENE *does "Chief of Love"*)

IRENE

Oh my chief of love,
You're my thief of love,
You left me so blue
Crying boo hoo boo hoo hoo hoo
Boo hoo hoo hoo hoo hoo hoo hoo.

Chief of love, sitting in your teepee,
Chief of love, sitting in your teepee,
Why did you leave your squaw so sad and weepy?
You've gone and strayed off the reservation,
You've gone and played off the reservation,
You broke the law of fair game conservation.
Love me only,
Your poor papoose is crying,
I'm so lonely
While on the loose you're flying.
Chief of love, with your eagle feather,
Chief of love, we belong together.
Oh please don't be an Indian giver,
Bring your arrows back to my quiver,
Come back home and I will deliver
Love, love, love, love,
You're my chief of love.

RUDY
(*Leaping up*)

Great, Irene!

JACK

She made it sound good.

HACKETT
(*Standing up slowly*)

Irene.

IRENE

Yes, Dick?

HACKETT

Have you got a ballad for us? Something soft and sweet?

IRENE

I've got a beautiful one, Dick. (*Picks up a piece of music, hands it to the pianist*) I think you'll like this.
  (*She goes center and starts to sing "I Could Have Danced All Night"*)

HACKETT
(*Standing up and interrupting her*)
Irene, you're hired! You're hired!

BLACKOUT

SCENE TWO

The bedroom in Stamford.
Night.
Frankie, in a dressing gown, is seated. She is reading a
playscript. Off stage the television set is blaring. A loud
announcer's voice.

ANNOUNCER'S VOICE
(Really loud)
Now remember, you late viewers. Please have consideration for
your neighbors and try to keep your volume down as low as possible. Now, back to our late movie in its first-run New York TV
debut, *The Cowboy and the Monster.*
(We hear screams, groans, grunts, dragging chains and
all the other noises of a horror movie. FRANKIE *gets up with*
the script in her hand. She goes to the left door and calls
out)

FRANKIE
Johnny. Johnny, it's late. Turn that off and go to bed. (*The*
sounds go off) I'm trying to read your father's script. (*To herself*
as she sits) At least it's got his name on it.
(She goes back to reading the script. JACK *enters hur-*
riedly. He looks like a man who is late. He takes off his hat,
throws it down, goes to FRANKIE, *leans over, puts his arm*
around her and gives her a small hug. For the first part of

89

*the following scene, * JACK *is full of excitement, elation and anxiety. He talks almost compulsively from excitement)*

JACK

I'm glad you're still up, honey. What a day, what a day! (*Looks at his watch*) Eleven-thirty. I'm sorry I blew dinner again, honey. Boy, what a crazy, tree-climbing business this is.

FRANKIE

Do you want some milk or coffee or something?

JACK

(*Pays no attention to her question*)

That office was a regular nuthouse today. Sketches, lawyers, agents. I was signing things in triplicate and fourplicate. I felt as if I was back in the army requisitioning paper clips. Then Irene came in and signed her contract, and Schatzie had photographers taking pictures of all of us hugging Irene and kissing her. Boy!

FRANKIE

Sounds like a grueling day.

JACK

And then we went over to Rex Dexter's apartment. Oh, I forgot to tell you — we got him. And does he look great.

FRANKIE

Rex Dexter? Why, he must be at least . . .

90

JACK

That's what I thought. But those movie guys really take care of themselves. He don't drink, he don't smoke, he don't do nothing.

FRANKIE

What part is he going to play?

JACK

Orville.

FRANKIE

Rex Dexter's going to play Uncle Orville?

JACK

What's wrong with that?

FRANKIE

I don't know . . . Every movie he's in looks like *Naughty Marietta*. You used to hate him.

JACK

Hackett thinks he'll be very good for the part. And he's a nice guy. We all went over to Sardi's and had a drink to celebrate. And then we went over to Twenty-one for dinner. What kind of an evening did you have? (FRANKIE *stares at him without answering and we see that she has been looking at him but not hearing him*) (*As if waking someone*) Frankie!

FRANKIE

(*Coming to*)

Huh? Oh, sorry. I was thinking.

JACK

What about?

FRANKIE

Well . . . Maybe it was a bum idea . . . I mean, me coming East and all that.

JACK

Look, honey, you're just bugged about being stuck up here in Stamford. Look, tomorrow night — Oh, hell. We've got a production meeting. Wednesday. You come in to town on Wednesday —
(FRANKIE *has been shaking her head during* JACK's *speech, and now she interrupts*)

FRANKIE

It isn't that, Jack. It's just that you have a lot of work to do and you shouldn't have to worry about me all the time . . . and I'm not doing any *good* here.

JACK

You sound just like your mother. (*Imitating mother*) "I guess I'm just in the way around here. I know when I'm not wanted."

FRANKIE

Well, she isn't wanted.

JACK

That's your mother, not you.

FRANKIE

Jack, I think the whole thing is crazy. You're going to be in rehearsal. You'll be dashing for the train all the time, and apologizing to me . . . And Christmas is coming . . . Incidentally, have you done anything about that trombone for Billy?

JACK

Billy?

FRANKIE

Your son.
(JACK *looks stunned.* FRANKIE *shakes her head wonderingly*)

JACK

All right. Don't look at me like that. I've got a lot on my mind. Damn it! Why do you have to get me upset like this right before rehearsal?
(*Exits left*)

FRANKIE

I don't understand you. You're like a man from outer space. (*Points to script*) Today when I read your script I . . .
(*She suddenly stops*)

JACK

Hey! It came.
(*Re-enters left*)

FRANKIE

The typist sent it this afternoon. (*Elaborately casual*) Well, I think I'll go to bed.
(*She takes off her robe, climbs into bed*)

93

JACK

It's pretty. (*Fondles script, holds it to his cheek*) First time I've ever seen it all in one hunk. Feels about ten minutes too long. Well, Frankie — (FRANKIE *is silent*) Frankie, you're not asleep. You said you were reading the script. What did you think?

FRANKIE

Well . . . I thought it was quite interesting. Had some good things in it.

JACK

You sound just like Ted Snow. "Quite interesting. Had some good things in it." Now why don't you tell me what you really think?

FRANKIE

Do you really want me to tell you what I really think?

JACK
(*Pause*)

No . . . Well, go ahead. Get out the meat axe. Let's have it. It's no good at all, huh?

FRANKIE

I wouldn't say that. It's slick, smooth, entertaining. But it doesn't sound like you.

JACK

Maybe you don't know me any more.

FRANKIE

Maybe I don't. But I do know about Uncle Orville. And he's lost in this story. Why, at the end you've got him leaving the river. Uncle Orville never left the river.

JACK

Damn it, Frankie. This is musical comedy.

FRANKIE

That's right. A musical comedy about Rosie. You even call it *The Girl from Indiana*. Now I can understand Rudy Lorraine handing the whole show to Irene. He used to be married to her.

JACK

Married to her?

FRANKIE

I assumed you knew.

. JACK

Why, she never said anything . . . How did you know that?

FRANKIE

You call yourself an educated, well-read man and you never look at a movie magazine. Irene was married to Rudy about six years ago. Then she was in love with that bullfighter, and then she was engaged to that Maharajah.

JACK

The poor kid. She's had a tough time.

FRANKIE

Oh, very tough.

JACK

Look, honey, you're not going to start getting jealous at your age.

FRANKIE

Thank you. Jack, I am not jealous of Miss Irene Lovelle. With all due respect to you, you ain't no bullfighter. I'm just concerned about your script.

JACK

I still say you don't like it because you're jealous of Irene Lovelle.

FRANKIE

Good night.

(*Puts out light*)

JACK

Good night. (*Goes off left*) Look, I think this is good. Richard Hackett thinks it's good. Ted Snow thinks it's good. Irene Lovelle thinks it's great. (*Re-enters*) Listen, smarty pants, I know more about this business than you'll ever know. (*We hear a loud bump, and* JACK *lets out a howl*) Oh, my toe. I broke my goddam toe. Frankie, can't you hear me — I broke my toe.

FRANKIE

Well — then the evening hasn't been a total loss.

BLACKOUT

96

SCENE THREE

Rehearsal scene, at a rehearsal hall.
Kids, Hackett, et al. discovered on stage.

HACKETT
(*Calling*)
Charlie. Charlie Williams!
(*General hubbub continues*)
(REX DEXTER *enters*)

IRENE

Rexy!

REX

Irene! Darling! (IRENE *hurls herself into his arms and they embrace*) (JACK *enters, goes upstage and starts phoning*) Hi, Rudy.

RUDY

Hey, Rexy boy.
(*Strikes up "Song of the Vagabonds"*)

REX

"Come all ye beggars of Paris town
Ye lousy rabble of low degree . . ."

(*Stops singing, addresses* RUDY *with good humor*)
You rat.

(*They stay at piano, talking*)

HACKETT

Charlie Williams!

(CHARLIE *goes among* KIDS, *settling them down, finally yells*)

CHARLIE

QUIET!

(JACK *is talking to* FRANKIE *on phone*)

JACK

Well, honey, you know the kind of guy Hackett is. He'll probably keep me here . . . (*His voice trails off as he realizes he is only one talking in the room*) Well, I've got to hang up now, honey. See you later. (*He hangs up.* HACKETT *watches him as he tiptoes to seat*) Sorry.

(HACKETT *gives* JACK *a look*)

HACKETT

(*Addressing group*)

Well, ladies and gentlemen . . . here we are. I'm sorry we have to rehearse in this cold warehouse, but we couldn't get into our theater right away, Mr. Snow tells me. During the next four weeks we are all going to be very, very busy. That goes for each of you, regardless of the size of your part. Now before we start this first reading, I have asked Mr. Lorraine to sing some of the songs so that those of you who haven't heard them can get the feel of the show. Our story concerns itself with the adventures

98

of a river boat captain at the turn of the century. He is hired
by a small traveling carnival to tow their barge down the river.

JACK

Up the river.

HACKETT

Up the river. (*Going on*) Our young handsome captain falls
in love, naturally, with the beautiful young girl from the carnival.
This leads to a lot of complications with her family, but it all
comes out all right . . . we hope. (*Holds his hand out to* RUDY)
Mr. Lorraine, if you please.

(*He sits*)

RUDY

I'll start out with a ballad. This is where Orville, the hero, pro-
poses to Rosie, the heroine, in the second act. It's called "Say,
Darling." Maurice —

(RUDY *sings "Say, Darling"*)

Say, darling,
May I offer you an invitation
To come to a little celebration I have planned for you.
There'll be music and wine and smiling faces,
There'll be flowers and friends from far-off places.
Say, darling,
The bells in the steeple will be ringing
And I'll take your hand and we'll go winging
To a lovely future.
Hey, darling,
Say, darling,
Say it's fine,
Say you're mine,
Say you'll say, darling, "I do."

(*After song,* CAST *applauds gently*)

99

Thank you. Now here's a number from the first act. Rosie, the carnival girl, is selling her patent medicine at the entrance to the sideshow. Say, Irene, why don't you sing this song?

(IRENE *gets up*)

HACKETT

That's a good idea, and, Jack, why don't you help her out by reading the barker's introduction in your finest Council Falls elocution.

JACK

Well, here's the way those old medicine guys used to do it: "Ladies and gentlemen and tiny tots, it's a great privilege to be here tonight in your salubrious city on the banks of the mighty Wabash. Permit me to introduce myself. I am Doctor Renaldo Rizzuto, graduate of the University of Heidelberg, and formerly personal physical to Her Majesty, Queen Lillolallaluau, beloved ruler of Hawaii. It was while working in the Islands that I discovered the magical properties of the bark of the yum-yum tree. From this bark I have prepared my famous medicine. Now here to tell you about it is my winsome little daughter, Rosie."

IRENE

(*Sings*)
The greatest boon to mankind since the dawn of time,
The cure that's guaranteed to make your life sublime,
The ancient magic formula of Egypt's sphinx,
One thousand wondrous miracles in this drink of drinks;
Good for anything that ails you,
Good for any function that fails you,
Makes you strong as a gladiator,
Dr. Rizzuto's Royal Rejuvo Regenerator.
It's good for a cold in the nose and the chest,

100

It's good to rub the egg-stain off your evening vest.
It's good for old folks and babies,
For snake bite, bubonic plague and rabies.
A bald man who drinks it will grow yards of hair.
It's good for shining shoes and cleaning silverware.
You can cook some meat in it,
Soak your feet in it.
Yes, the product above
Is even good for unrequited love.

(*Spoken*)

Yes, ladies and gentlemen, there isn't anyone in this crowd who
can*not* be helped by this fabulous elixir, and I want to say . . .

MAN

(*Interrupting, holding cane, old man's voice*)
I say there, can this Dr. Rizzuto's Royal Rejuvo Regenerator
do anything for a terrible case of lumbago?

IRENE

(*Giving him bottle*)
Yes, sir! You just take a sip of this and . . .

MAN

(*Taking bottle*)
Well, I don't know . . . I'm very skeptical . . . very doubt-
ful . . . (*He sips, bursts into wild frenetic dance*) It's good!
(*Sits*)

IRENE

There you are, folks, a perfect stranger.

(*Sung*)

Need I say more!!!
It's good for your grandpa, it's good for your child.
Just spray it as a perfume and the boys go wild.
It's a magical medicine, mellow and mild.

(*Spoken*)

And furthermore, ladies and gentlemen . . .

(*Sung*)

You can baste a goose with it,
Stuff a moose with it.
Paint your living room wall.
For just one dollar,
You'll be delighted,
You'll be excited.
Just one dollar,
You'll be ignited,
The price is right,
It's ninety-six point seven alcohol.
So step up, folks, it's good for one and all!

HACKETT

Take five everybody. And then we'll get to work.
(KIDS *scatter.* REX *crosses to* JACK)

REX

Jordan, your script reads awfully well.

JACK

Thank you, Mr. Dexter.

REX

Rex, my boy, Rex. (*Turns to* IRENE) Irene, I can't wait until I
face a live audience again.

IRENE

I'm with you, kid.

REX

No more Hollywood for me. I'm going to stay here forever. And thank heavens, Mother loves New York.

(*He goes*)

JACK

Isn't this a great gang? Everybody's so friendly.

IRENE

Enjoy it while you can, because in a very short while, none of us will be talking to each other.

JACK

I don't believe that.

IRENE

Jack, I'm just crazy about you.

JACK

I don't believe that either.

IRENE

Say, we're not rehearsing tonight. How about buying me dinner?

JACK

Hey, great. (*Sudden take*) Oh, oh . . . I can't tonight.

IRENE

Working?

JACK

No, it's just that I sort of promised my wife . . .

IRENE

I understand.

JACK

You see, she's meeting me in town and we're going to go out . . . do the town.

IRENE

Sounds like fun.

JACK

You see, Frankie hasn't been getting to town much and I thought . . .

IRENE

Jack, please. I do understand. The way you're explaining this, anyone would think that *I* was your wife. Why don't you have her come to rehearsal sometime?

JACK

Well, it's kind of hard for her to get in on account of the kids and all. And, besides, Frankie doesn't understand about musical comedy. It's a whole different world for her.

IRENE

I'd like to meet her. What's she like?

JACK

Frankie? Oh, she's okay, I guess.

IRENE

Does your wife know you go around raving about her like this all the time?

JACK

Oh, don't get me wrong . . . Look, Frankie's a good-looking kid.

(HACKETT *enters*)

HACKETT

Say, Jack, when you hear the script read today, listen carefully to the second scene. I want to cut that way down.

JACK

Gee, Dick, there's hardly anything left there now. If we're going to have any relationship between Orville and Rosie, we really need to . . .

HACKETT

(*Cutting him off*)

Jack, this is musical comedy. The scene is too talky. Got to be cut.

JACK

Well, Dick, if you say so.

HACKETT

We'll work on it tonight.

105

JACK
(*Startled*)

Tonight?

HACKETT

Yep. We should get at this right away. Meet me at the office at eight o'clock. We'll be through by ten.

JACK

But I didn't think we'd have to work tonight.

IRENE

You're a slave driver, Dick. He has a date with his wife.

HACKETT

Too bad, family man. See you at eight.
(*He walks away*)

JACK
(*Sighing*)
Well, might as well call Frankie and tell her not to come in.

IRENE

She could come in for dinner and go home afterward.

JACK

It's too far, just for dinner. That wouldn't be fair to her. I'll just call it off and have dinner with you.
(*Lights dim*)

ANNOUNCEMENT

Wednesday, December sixth. Miss Lovelle with Mr. Lorraine and Mr. Hackett.

(Lights come up)

RUDY

No, no, no — that's not right. Can't you get it through that thick skull of yours?

IRENE

It sounds right to me.

RUDY

Well, it's not right. Please try it again.

IRENE

(Sings)

Say, darling —

RUDY

(Sings)

The bells in the steeple will be ringing
And I'll take your hand and we'll go winging
To a lovely future.
Hey, darling —

IRENE

(Sings wrong note)

Say, darling —

RUDY

No, that's not right. But I'm not worried because I know you're going to get it. All right, let's try it again.

(*Sings*)
Hey, darling . . . say, darling — say, darling —

(*Spoken*)
Have you got it? (IRENE *shrugs*) All right, Maurice, from the same place.

(MAURICE *plays*, RUDY *sings*)
Hey, darling —

IRENE
(*Wrong note*)
Say, darling —

(RUDY *slaps the piano, impatiently*)
Well, I like it better my way.

RUDY
If I'd wanted it sung that way, I'd have *written* it that way!
(REX *enters*)

HACKETT
All right, cut it out now. Here's Rex. (*To* REX) Rex, here's what this session's about. Rudy and I feel that "Say, Darling" in scene three will be much stronger as a duet with Irene.

REX
(*Very cool to the idea*)
Oh. Really?

RUDY
Look, this will make more sense — and I've got it all figured out harmonically.

108

REX

Well, if Irene feels that she needs another number . . .

IRENE

Let's not be bitchy, Rex dear. It was Rudy's decision to put me in the song.

RUDY

Let's cut out this hambo jazz and get to work.

REX

Very well.

HACKETT

And don't sulk.

REX

I am not sulking.

RUDY

Now, look, Rex, I'll show you how this works. You start the second half, and I'll show you where Irene comes in.

REX
(*Sings*)

Say, darling,
The bells in the steeple will be ringing
And I'll take your hand and we'll go winging
To a lovely future.
Hey, darling . . .
(*He nods to Irene*)

IRENE
(*Wrong note*)

Say, darling . . .

109

RUDY

No, no, no!

(*Sings*)

Hey, darling.

IRENE

(*Wrong note*)

Say, darling . . .

RUDY

You tin-eared idiot!

(*He slaps her in a rage*)

IRENE

(*To Hackett*)

He hit me. He hit me. Make him apologize.

HACKETT

Apologize.

RUDY

(*To* REX)

Rex, I apologize.

(*Blackout. In the black, we hear*)

ANNOUNCEMENT

Monday, December eleventh. Miss Lovelle with Mr. Hackett, Mr. Lorraine, and Mr. Jordan.

HACKETT

That's not it.

IRENE

Not it at all!

JACK

That's what I got here.
(*Stage lights up and* RUDY, HACKETT *and* IRENE *are at the piano.* JACK *is standing near them holding a yellow pad and a pencil*)

HACKETT

No, Jack, no.

IRENE

You've got it wrong.

JACK

What do you mean, I've got it wrong?

RUDY

Yeah, you got it *all* wrong.

JACK

Now wait a minute. Let's get this straight. You want a tongue on rye, you want a swiss on whole wheat . . .

IRENE

Two swiss on whole wheat.

JACK

Coffee?

111

RUDY

Black.

IRENE

Tea, with lemon.

HACKETT

Yogurt.

JACK
(*Going off*)
My God, they've even got me rewriting the delicatessen.

(*Blackout*)

ANNOUNCEMENT
Mr. Reshevsky and dancers in Room 4.
(*Lights come up*)
(JACK *is on phone talking to* FRANKIE)

JACK

Look, honey, I've just got a minute till Hackett and the others get here. Look, honey, about tonight . . . we start late rehearsals tonight. I don't know when we're going to finish . . . and I have to be up early in the morning. What? I had better stay in town, don't you think? Huh? No, I didn't get over to Schwarz's. Look, what the hell does Johnny want a sled for? There's no snow in Connecticut. Look, honey, I'm sorry. You're going to have to do the worrying about Christmas this year. All I can do is be there. Huh? What kind of a crack is that? Of course I want to be there. Look, honey, the people are here. I gotta go now. Tell the kids good night for me. I'll call you tomorrow. 'By. (*Hangs up*) Say,

Dick . . . (HACKETT *looks at him*) We *are* going to be off on
Christmas, aren't we?

HACKETT
(*Indignantly*)
We're doing a show! (*Then he becomes reluctantly generous*)
Well, I suppose you can take it off, if you have to.

(BORIS *crosses to* JACK)
Say, Jack . . .

JACK
Just call me Bob Cratchit.
(*He goes*)

BORIS
(*To* HACKETT)
What's with him?

HACKETT
He's a family man. Now let's get to work. I'll be with you in
a minute.
(*He goes*)

BORIS
All right, kids. Let's get to work on the husking bee.
(KIDS *break up and* TED SNOW, *who has been concealed,
comes out*)

TED
My place around nine.
(*He starts off*)

113

BORIS

Mr. Snow, if you're not too busy, I'd like you to watch this section.

TED

Fine.

BORIS

(*To the* KIDS)

Now, yesterday I gave you some steps to the husking bee. Today, let's put it together and see what we've got. Meet me at the husking bee — six, seven, eight. (*They start dance, get mixed up, stop*) That was my fault, kids. Let's start over. The girls go upstage, the boys downstage. Now. Meet me at the husking bee — six, seven, eight.

(*They dance until* TED *interrupts them*)

TED

Say, Boris . . . Boris, I hate interrupting you, but this dance . . . isn't it a bit too . . . too . . . well, pedestrian? I mean, when I, that is, when we hired you, I thought with your background we'd get something more . . . well . . . expressive. Right here I'd love to feel the grandeur and elegance of the real ballet.

BORIS

Well, Mr. Snow, I've been working on another section you might like. The kids haven't learned it yet, but I'll show you how some of it goes. This is the girls' section. Peter . . .

(BORIS *starts his solo. During dance,* TED, *obviously enthusiastic, calls out "Bravo!" several times.* HACKETT *enters, stands there watching* BORIS)

114

HACKETT
(*Interrupting*)

What's that, Boris?

BORIS

It's part of the husking bee.

HACKETT

Who told you to do that? I don't like it. Why, if anybody danced like that at a Middle Western husking bee, they'd get lynched. You'd better change it.

BORIS

Well, I've got another section I'd like to show you.

HACKETT

I'd like to see it.
(BORIS *and* KIDS *go into first jazzy section*)

BORIS

All right, boys and girls, let's do the first section. Meet me at the husking bee — six, seven, eight.
(*They dance*)

HACKETT

Good, Boris. Very good. Don't you think so, Ted?

TED

Oh, yes. Very exciting. Very exciting.
(*Exits*)

CLOSE IN

Scene Four

Bedroom in Stamford.

Late afternoon.

Off stage we hear the sound of a television set making Western noises — horses' hoofs, guns, bullets whining, etc. We see some children's toys lying around and some Christmas gifts in the process of being wrapped. Frankie enters from the side the set's playing on. She is all dressed up to go out, dinner dress, earrings, fur, the works.

FRANKIE

Now remember what I said. That goes off at nine o'clock. (*She starts going off. Phone rings. She stops and stares at it. It rings again. She goes to it as though it were some ugly black beast. Finally, she picks it up, speaks into it*) Hello, Jack . . . Oh, I knew it was you. What? Oh, I understand. Well, if we can't make it, we can't. No, it's all right. I haven't gone to any trouble. All right, dear, call me tomorrow. 'By. (*Hangs up phone, sits on bed*) I hate show business. I hate Irene Lovelle. I hate Connecticut. I hate the Merritt Parkway. I hate station wagons. I hate Gristede Brothers.

BLACKOUT

116

Scene Five

Irene's apartment.

Evening.

The scene is the living room. It is very lush and pretty. It should look like Irene. A small piano should be visible and a bar. Upstage center is a fireplace. Facing it is a large sofa which has its back to the audience. There is also some form of Christmas decoration; either a small tree or a wreath, or whatever.

Irene Lovelle enters, carrying a bottle of bourbon. She hums as she sets it on the bar, and arranges the glassware. There is a knock on the door. Irene goes off, and returns with Jack Jordan.

JACK

Hey, some layout . . . this is great.

IRENE

I've been trying to lure you up here for weeks.

JACK

My father always told me to stay out of girls' apartments. Especially city girls. And you look like a city girl to me.

IRENE

Oh, I'm one of the worst.

117

JACK

Well . . . I have to make the five-thirty-two.

IRENE
(*Comes up to him holding a drink*)

Here.

JACK
(*Backing away from the drink*)
I don't know if I should. I've already had a few.
(IRENE *keeps holding drink out*)

IRENE

Okay.

JACK

Well. (*Taking the drink*) Just one quick one. (*Drinks some of the drink*) I just have to make the five-thirty-two. I haven't been home for three days. Maybe guys who write shows shouldn't be married. (*As* JACK *wanders, he falls into his old habit of inspecting the millwork. Inspects mantelpiece. Then he looks at doorframe and door. Suddenly stops like an art connoisseur who has discovered a missing El Greco*) Hey! This is one of our doors. Look at that. That's the Johnson Sash and Door Number Four-forty-six, Three-panel Ponderosa Special.

IRENE

I've been saving it for a surprise.

JACK
(*Addressing the door affectionately*)
Well, little old Four-forty-six. Sure never thought I'd run into you again — especially on Park Avenue. Here's to you! (IRENE

has made another drink during his speech. She now brings over the fresh one and takes his empty glass) I shouldn't. If I miss the five-thirty-two, Frankie will never forgive me. I haven't even called her today.

IRENE

Just tell her you ran into a door.

JACK

(*Looks at the drink, takes a slug*)

Well, I can always get the six-oh-eight. Frankie'll understand. (*Stops*) No, she won't . . . She's been kind of nervous lately. I'm kind of jumpy, myself. (*Finishes drink*) I don't know how I ever got mixed up in this business. I ought to be back at the mill counting knotholes.

(*Mixing drink*)

IRENE

Counting what?

JACK

Knotholes. You can't use the lumber for anything until you get the knots out of it. You gotta spot them, and then a fellow cuts them out. He works in the cutting room at a great circular saw, and he goes *Zzzzzzooooom*.

IRENE

Hey, watch it, you'll get sawdust all over the place. Look, forget about the knotholes — you're a playwright, and you belong in New York.

JACK

I don't know. Uncle Orville always said, "Son, if the Good Lord meant for normal folks to live in New York City, he would have put the damn fool town in Wisconsin in the first place."

IRENE

Oh, cut that yokel bit. Half New York comes from out there someplace. You'll get used to it.

JACK

I wonder if I ever will. I'm really not with it. I sit around Sardi's with you folks, and I don't know what anybody's talking about. I hang around at rehearsals. I don't really do anything. Every time I open my mouth, Hackett says, "Jack, this is musical comedy." I never get a word in. And when I do get to say something, you're the only one who listens.

IRENE

I respect the things you say.

JACK

Irene, I'm not very big with the sweet talk — but I'm sure glad I got to know you.

IRENE

Well, Jack, maybe you don't understand what knowing you has meant to me. I've been floundering . . . my career . . . men . . . phonies . . . When someone real and honest comes along, it's . . .

(*She stops*)

SAY, DARLING

JACK

Irene, this is a terrible thing to say, but I think I'm in love with you.

IRENE
(*Tenderly*)

No, Jack. No, you're not.

JACK

It certainly feels like it.

IRENE
(*Shaking her head*)

It's just that you're worried and unhappy and — I'm here.

JACK

All I know is, I've never met anyone like you, and I've never felt like this about anyone else.

IRENE

Jack, you're very sweet. You're very attractive. But . . . (JACK *puts his arms around her and kisses her — a long kiss.* IRENE *finally pulls away*) Whew! Maybe you'd better make that train.

JACK

There's one at seven-oh-two.

(*He kisses her again. After a moment they sink down on the couch out of view. After a few seconds . . .*)

TED
(*Off*)

I could sure use a drink.

SCHATZIE
(*Off*)

Me, too.

RUDY
(*Off. Calling*)

Irene?

SCHATZIE
(*Off*)

Maybe she didn't get home yet.

RUDY

The door was open. (*They enter.* TED *carries a bottle of champagne.* IRENE *stands up*) Irene! Irene, what were you doing? (JACK *stands up*) Oh.

IRENE

Jack and I were just sitting here looking at the fire.

SCHATZIE

What fire? The fire ain't even lit.

RUDY

Maybe they were trying out a new way to light one.

TED

(*Tearing wrapping off the bottle of champagne*)
While we're talking, this beautifully chilled wine is getting warm. (*He looks at the bottle*) Look at that. Bollinger forty-three. There's very little of this stuff left. Get the glasses, Irene.

IRENE
(*Going off*)

Coming up.

(*She goes*)
(*They all stare at* JACK, *who looks sheepish*)

JACK

Hey, my watch stopped. What time is it?

SCHATZIE

Six-thirty. What train you making?

JACK

Well, I guess if I leave now I can still make the eight-oh-seven.

TED

Well, one more week and we're in New Haven. It's been fun, hasn't it, Jordan?

JACK

Loads.

(IRENE *enters with four glasses. She hands one to everybody but* RUDY)

123

TED

You know, I'm already thinking about our next show. I'm in the process of negotiating for a very interesting property.

RUDY

What is it?

TED

I don't want this to get around, but I'm trying to acquire the rights to a new book that I think will make a great musical. It's an eye-witness account of Sir Edmund Hillary's dash to the South Pole.

RUDY

You're nuts.

JACK

Might not be so bad — you could call it *Charlie's Antarctica*.

TED

You guys have no imagination.

IRENE

Now come on, let's have a drink.

JACK

Where's Rudy's drink?

IRENE

Rudy never drinks. He's afraid he might let his hair down.

RUDY

I just think it makes people sloppy.

TED

(*Starting to pour*)

Well, let's all get sloppy. Good luck, everybody. (RUDY *starts playing "Silent Night." Everybody else drinks the champagne.* JACK *gulps his down like a shot of whisky*) Hey, easy, boy. This isn't red-eye. It's a delicate wine.

JACK

(*Grabs bottle from* IRENE, *pours drink*)

Where I come from, hooch is hooch.

TED

Why, Rudy, you're being sentimental.

IRENE

He just likes that because it's a big hit song.

(JACK *slowly sinks down onto the sofa and disappears from view. The others don't notice*)

IRENE

(*Looking around*)

Hey, where's Jack? (*They start to look for* JACK, *and all converge on the sofa and look down at him*) (*Tenderly*) Isn't that sweet?

SCHATZIE

What did he have to drink before the delicate wine?

IRENE

Several double bourbons.

SCHATZIE

He may be dead.

RUDY

Not *that* country boy. It's probably just his bedtime.

IRENE

He got all excited because he found one of his doors. Maybe we should wake him up. His wife is expecting him home.

SCHATZIE

Well, his wife ain't going to like it if he comes home asphyxiated.

TED

Better let him sleep it off. Schatzie, we're going to be late. Let's go.

SCHATZIE

So long, Irene.

TED

Rudy, we're going uptown. Can we drop you?

RUDY
(*Carefully*)
Uh . . . I'll stick around and keep the party going.

IRENE

You just got here.

TED

Sorry, dear. Hackett asked us to meet him tonight at his place.
(*Shrugging*) He says it's important.

SCHATZIE

He probably wants us to trim his tree. (TED *exits*) So that's a
shatzendoor.

(*Exits*)
(RUDY *and* IRENE *are left alone. They seem somewhat
embarrassed by this — almost like two honeymooners,
avoiding each other's eyes.* RUDY *is playing something at
the piano.* IRENE *stands near the piano and listens*)

RUDY

Hey, Irene, what's with you and Huckleberry Finn?

IRENE
(*Unprepared*)

Huh?

RUDY

When we walked in on you two, you looked as if you had just
got back from the mooooon.

IRENE

Rudy, that was . . . a tender moment. Something you couldn't
possibly understand.

RUDY

Are you stuck on him?

IRENE

(*With a gentle smile*)

Well . . . I guess not . . . but he's the kind of man I would be stuck on, if I had any brains. He's a nice guy . . . warm . . . gentle.

(*There is a long pause as* RUDY *thinks this over*)

RUDY

I'm sorry I belted you the other day.

IRENE

(*With a despairing sigh*)

That's all right.

RUDY

I guess I should have apologized sooner, but . . . that kind of thing is murder for me. I don't know why.

IRENE

I know why, Rudy. You're pretty good with a fast line or a clever lyric — but when it comes to saying what you really feel — boom, the shades come down, the door slams, and you're closed for the night.

RUDY

A guy can't go around spilling his guts all the time.

128

IRENE

It's not spilling your guts to let someone know how you feel. I remember how it was with us back in Hollywood . . .
 (*She shakes her head*)

RUDY

We had laughs.

IRENE

Yes. We had laughs. We were laughing all the time, but we never were close.

RUDY
 (*Startled*)

Never close?

IRENE

I don't mean close that way. I never knew you. I never knew how you felt about me or anything else.

RUDY

All I know is, whatever we had — I miss it.

IRENE

Well, I don't miss it. Meant nothing . . . had no point . . . had no . . .
 (RUDY *grabs* IRENE *and kisses her hard. She kisses him back*)

RUDY

Look, baby, let's get out of here and go someplace.

129

IRENE

What about Huckleberry Finn?

RUDY

Oh, we'll leave him a note.
(*Walks to piano — picks up Christmas card and pencil —
starts writing*)

IRENE

Where'll we go?

RUDY

We'll go over to the East Side. One of those classy joints, where
they make with the candlelight and fiddles — the whole romance
bit.

IRENE

I'll get my coat. Here I go again.
(*Exit*)

(*Left traveler opens revealing* FRANKIE, *ready to travel.
She is sitting in the chair in the Stamford bedroom writing
a farewell note to* JACK)
(*In* IRENE'S *apartment,* RUDY *crosses to sofa and puts card
on* JACK'S *wrist*)

RUDY

Farewell, O Chief of Love.
(*Exit*)

FRANKIE

(*Leaves note on chair. Rises, crosses left, looks back,
speaks as if to* JACK)

Good-by, honey.

> (*Close in left traveler*)
> (*Time passes.* JACK *awakens, rises*)

JACK

(*Reading*)

Dear Jack. This is to be sung roughly to the tune of "Jingle Bells." (*Stops a moment to recall the tune of "Jingle Bells"*) Oh, yeah. (*He sings the following*)

> Jackie boy, Jackie boy,
> It's my painful duty
> To tell you that Irene loves me —
> Merry Christmas, Rudy.

CURTAIN

131

ACT THREE

ACT THREE

Scene One

A hotel suite in New Haven. Time is night, right after the opening performance. A waiter is arranging some bottles and set-ups on the desk.
Rudy enters, lost in solemn thought.

WAITER

How was the opening tonight, Mr. Lorraine? (RUDY *does not respond*) Oh.
(He exits)
(SCHATZIE *enters, followed by* HACKETT. *They sit.* TED *enters, singing "Say, Darling")*

TED

Well, not bad, not bad at all.
(They all look at him for a moment)

HACKETT

What wasn't bad?

TED

The show. A little long, but it went very well.

135

RUDY

What show did you see tonight, *The Ten Commandments?*

TED

All right, I admit there are some problems, but that's why we're in New Haven. Where's Jack?

SCHATZIE

He's trying to get his wife on the phone, in Iowa — Idaho, or someplace.

TED

Look, fellows, Morty Krebs is coming up in a few minutes and I don't want him to get too depressed about the show.

RUDY

Morty Krebs? Why?

HACKETT

Ted, must we have him up here? He'll be giving us a million notes and suggestions. We've got enough troubles.

TED

Morty's a very shrewd man.

HACKETT

He may be shrewd at making soap . . .

TED

Not soap, Dick, detergents. He's got a lot of money in this

show, so I think we can at least be courteous to him. Besides, I don't think we're in all that trouble.

SCHATZIE

I kinda go along with Ted. I think we got a chance. Now here's what I think for what it's worth. Get in a few more good-looking broads, show the audience some legs, take about a half-hour out of the first act, get a new opening number, fix that second act, get a whole, entire new finale, and you're a smash.

HACKETT

Is anybody taking this down?

TED

Of course, the show didn't quite build as I had anticipated. I was aware of a diminishing audience response.

HACKETT

Well, let's put it this way, Ted. They didn't like it.

TED

Well, they didn't hate us.

HACKETT

I don't know. I just saw a bunch of fellows down in the lobby. They were carrying a rope and asking for your room number.
(JACK *enters, sits at desk*)

TED

I can't say I appreciate your gallows humor.

RUDY

Well, they did hate the show, Mr. Snow, and I'll tell you why. The book didn't work, so my numbers never had a chance. You couldn't hear my lyrics, the orchestra drowned them out. That guy ain't no conductor, he's a goddam drum major.

TED

Now, wait a minute, Rudy. You okayed Maurice yourself. He's a fine, sensitive musician.

RUDY

He's a fine, sensitive bum.

TED

Rudy, for your information . . . (MORTY KREBS *enters*) Hold it, here's Morty. (*He rushes over to* MORTY, *beaming*) Hello, Morty.

MORTY

Hello, Ted. Hi, boys.

RUDY

Hi.

HACKETT

Hello.

TED

Have a drink, Morty?

138

MORTY

Yes. I'll have a little vodka and cranberry juice.

TED

Cranberry juice?

MORTY

You don't have any? Well then, give me something simple —
just give me some plain Scotch and Pepsi-Cola.

TED

(*Starting to mix drink*)
Well, Morty, what did you think?

MORTY

Well, my opinion doesn't count for much — I'm a businessman.
When I back a show, I'm not backing a show — I'm putting my
money on people. (*Pointing to the four of them*) On you, on
you, on you, on you.

TED

That's the kind of thinking we appreciate, Morty.

MORTY

Sure. Who am I to tell you how to fix a show? This old bastard
has been around for a hundred years. Me, like I say, I'm a
businessman. But I thought out of pure friendship, I ought to
make a few notes.
(*He takes a big sheaf of papers from his breast pocket*)

TED

Swell. We'll sure appreciate any suggestions you have, Morty. Won't we, fellows?

(*The others look as if they won't*)

HACKETT AND RUDY

Yeah.

MORTY

By the way, Rudy, have you made a deal for European rights to the songs?

RUDY

Not yet.

MORTY

I've got a tax gimmick that's out of this world. I won't give you details, but you press the disks in Zurich and you ship them to London by way of Tangiers. Then you collapse the whole corporation and have a capital gain in Swiss francs. You don't like it! Well, here's another one. You incorporate yourself in Winnipeg and then . . .

RUDY

Winnipeg?

TED

Morty, please — let's get back to the show.

MORTY

Okay. Well, my first note is . . . Now you know I'm a businessman . . . Business consists of merchandising. To me a show is like any other product. It's got to be merchandised. Think of Broadway as a big supermarket. On one shelf, over here, is *My*

140

Fair Lady. Another shelf, your show. Over there, *West Side Story*. Over there, *Auntie Mame*. The shelves are full of shows. Say I'm your average customer. I walk into the supermarket. What would make me want to select your show over the others?

RUDY

Because we give green stamps?

MORTY

(*Annoyed*)

Well, if you want to make jokes.

TED

Rudy's just kidding. Go on, Morty. This is very interesting.

MORTY

What would make me want to select your show is packaging. Packaging is the heart and soul of merchandising. Take my business. We put out a shampoo for the ladies. It's called Glamour-Poo. Used to be packaged in a jar. Couldn't sell it at all. Then we put it into a tube — a pink and gold tube. Wham! Today it's the biggest thing in hair. Now, that's what you've got to do with your show.

HACKETT

Stuff it in a tube.

MORTY

You guys are full of jokes tonight.

TED

No, go on, Morty. How does this tie up with our show?

141

MORTY

You got to package it. Give it the glitter that we gave to Glamour-Poo. Now, tell me, Ted, straight from the shoulder. Do you think you've provided this show with the proper packaging?

TED

I think so.

MORTY

Fine. Now my next note. (*Turns to* RUDY) Rudy. Rudy. You've done a fine job. Nice tunes, peppy lyrics — but only one thing, Rudy. You know what I miss?

RUDY

What?

MORTY

I miss . . . (*Sings*) "Some enchanted evening . . ."

RUDY

"Some enchanted evening"? What the hell does that have to do with me?

MORTY

Don't knock it, Rudy. It was a great song. (*Sings*) "Some enchanted evening . . ."

HACKETT

Mr. Krebs, I don't see any point in discussing songs from other shows.

MORTY

It was a beautiful song . . . (GIRLS *enter*) . . . and you need something like it in this show.

GIRLS

Is this where the party is?

SCHATZIE

Does this look like a party?

TED

No, girls. The kids are all on the seventh floor. Hey, Morty, all the chorus kids are having a party. Why don't you look in on it? I'll join you in a minute.

MORTY

I still got quite a few notes. I haven't even started on the book yet.

TED

Come on, Morty. Save them for later. And there'll be a lot of beautiful girls. It'll be good for morale.

MORTY

Well, if it'll be good for morale, I'll go. Besides, I have a feeling that you guys don't care what I think of the show, anyway.

TED

That's not true, Morty. Your notes have been very valuable. But what we really want from you is your over-all feeling about the show. Before you go, Morty, tell us — Did you like it?

MORTY

Ted, I got where I am by being honest, straight from the shoulder. You ask me did I like the show. I'll lay it on the line, without beating around the bush. I did, and I didn't. See you later.

(MORTY *and the* GIRLS *go*)

RUDY

He sure was a help.

TED

Never mind Morty. Now about the show. Rudy, if you were a little more tolerant . . .

RUDY

If you weren't so . . .

HACKETT

Now, boys. Quiet down. I don't think this is a bad show, but the audience didn't buy it, and we have to assume that it was our fault.

RUDY

Well, it wasn't *my* fault. My stuff's okay. Maybe needs a little polishing.

HACKETT

A little polishing, eh? Here's a program. I've checked off the numbers that I think are going to have to be replaced.

RUDY

(*Looking at program in horror*)

You're kidding. You even checked off "Say, Darling." You're not planning to cut "Say, Darling"?

144

HACKETT

It won't work in this show, Rudy.

RUDY

You can't cut it. Dinah Shore just recorded it. Eddie Fisher's going to make a record. Perry Como. The Crew Cuts. The Everly Brothers . . . (BORIS *enters. He goes to refreshment table and fixes a drink*) This is crazy! All the songs are good. They were played wrong, sung wrong, danced wrong . . . (RUDY *points at* BORIS) Yes, danced wrong.

BORIS

We have no room. How can we dance when we have no room? Those sets were impossible to dance in.

TED

Now just a minute, Boris . . .

RUDY

Boris is right, Ted. Those sets looked as if they were cut out of a cornflakes box.

TED

(*Blowing high*)

Goddam it, Rudy, I think this is a very handsomely mounted production, and I resent any implication that the management has in any way stinted on this production, costume-wise, scenery-wise, cast-wise, or any other way-wise. The trouble with you, Rudy, is that you are, without a doubt . . .

145

RUDY

(*Jumping in*)

I don't know how I ever got mixed up in this whole lousy set-up. The only thing that works in this show is my score and I've got a good mind to pull the whole score right out of the show.

TED

(*All together*)

All I know is the management has fulfilled every obligation. Everything was chosen with care and taste, without regard to cost or expense.

BORIS

All I know is we got no room to dance and we got nothing to dance about.

SCHATZIE

When a guy comes to a show he wants to see broads, that's what he wants to see.

JACK

(*Suddenly lets out a yell*)

Ohhh, crud!

(*Everybody stops and looks at him*)

TED

(*Stunned*)

What was that?

JACK

(*Getting up*)

I felt it was time for me to participate in this symposium. So

146

I said . . . "Crud." That's my contribution. It seems to be the *mot juste*.

(JACK *starts to pour himself a drink*)

HACKETT
Jack, I'd go easy on the liquor tonight, if I were you.

JACK
Oh, I'm not going to drink much. Just enough to get stiff.

HACKETT
We'll have to meet bright and early tomorrow morning — around nine o'clock. You'll want your head nice and clear.

JACK
You don't have to worry about my little head. You see . . . I'm not going to meet you.

HACKETT
(*Cautiously*)

You're not?

JACK
Dick, nobody seems to know what was wrong tonight. But there is one thing I do know. The people up there on that stage don't sound like the people I wrote about in my book.

HACKETT
Jack, I have a lot of thoughts on the dialogue. In the first place . . .

JACK
(*Holding his hands over his ears*)
Please, Dick. Let me use my own skull. So far I've been a

147

writing machine. You put in a quarter and out comes a line and three cents change.

HACKETT
(*Conciliatory*)

Now, Jack, I understand how you feel. Every author needs a chance to meditate. I'll tell you what — Why don't you go ahead. Think things out as much as you want to, and then meet me at ten-thirty.

JACK

Dick, you don't understand. I've got to get away from you for a couple of days. I want to do my thinking by myself, and I'm going to do it in Stamford.

TED
(*Shocked*)

Stamford!

JACK

Yep. The vibrations are all wrong here. You see, that little honeymoon cottage you got me in Stamford is now empty. No wife. No kids. I'll have nothing to do but think.

HACKETT

Jack, I think we should all tackle this problem together. We've made some mistakes, but we haven't time to make many more.

TED

I should say we haven't. If we're going to think, let's all think together and get this show fixed. We've got all those theater

148

parties booked, and advance sales . . . Now, Jack, I'd like to tell you something.

JACK

I don't want you to tell me anything. Everybody's been telling me things for three months now. My head is so full of instructions, it feels like an overripe watermelon. I wasn't in New York ten minutes when you started telling me. You told me to sit down and you told me my book was just dandy. Then you told me that the state of Wisconsin was actually in southern Indiana and that the Chippewa River was really the Wabash. Next you knocked me down and sat on my chest and told me that Indians are lousy box office, for God's sakes, and because of that, my Uncle Orville's girl is a redheaded, blue-eyed Sicilian from the suburbs of Naples. You told me, you told me, and now there's only one thing anybody can tell me.

TED

What?

JACK

Where the hell's the bathroom?
(TED *points.* JACK *starts for the bathroom*)

HACKETT

Now listen, Jack.

JACK
(*Stopping him with upraised hand*)
No! I'm going alone.
(*He goes*)

TED

Well, that was an exhibition!

SCHATZIE

I wish I could print it.

(*Exits*)

HACKETT

Ted, I've been working with writers for years. They all need special handling. At the moment, I think Jordan needs to be given his head. It's good psychology.

RUDY

I always wondered what you theater people discussed in these top-secret hotel room meetings. Now I know . . . nothing. All everybody did was pick on my songs and then we had to listen to Jack Jordan making a graduation speech.

HACKETT

Maybe he is graduating. And maybe you will, too, if you do a little of his kind of thinking.

RUDY

I'll do my own kind of thinking. And my own kind of thinking tells me to think about calling my lawyer.

HACKETT

Rudy, there's no use in calling your lawyer unless he can write songs.

RUDY

Oh, God. (*He looks ill, goes to sofa, sits*) Oh, God. Maybe you've got the wrong guy. Maybe I can't write a show.

150

TED

Don't say that, Rudy.

HACKETT

Look, Ted, go and join Morty. (TED *goes*) Rudy, I think you can.

RUDY

My dear pals on Broadway are sure going to have a good time at this funeral. Oh, God.

(IRENE *enters during this speech*)

IRENE
(*To* HACKETT)

What's with him?

HACKETT

New Haven neurosis. Real tough guys are particularly susceptible.

RUDY

Irene, I'm licked.

IRENE

No, you're not. You're just scared out of your Tin Pan Alley wits.

RUDY

I tell you I'm licked. Washed up.

IRENE

Rudy, this is the wrong time for you to stop being an egomaniac.

RUDY

(*Leaps up*)

He wants about eighty-nine new songs. I don't think there's another idea left in my head. He's out of his mind.

IRENE

You're lucky to have Dick here to help you. Trust him, Rudy. He knows what he's doing.

RUDY

He wants to take "Say, Darling" out of the show.

IRENE

(*To* HACKETT)

You're out of your mind!

. HACKETT .

We should have something stronger down there, Irene.

IRENE

(*Thinking it over*)

Well, I wouldn't mind having a bigger number in that spot.

RUDY

(*Snapping*)

I haven't got a bigger number.

IRENE

Maybe something warmer. I'm supposed to be in love with Orville, but the songs we sing to each other . . . Rudy, if you ask me . . .

RUDY

Nobody's asking you.

IRENE

I see. I'm just an actor. I'm supposed to take every silly song you give me and stand up there singing them with egg on my face.

RUDY

Tonight you sang them with mush in your mouth.

HACKETT

Now cut that out, Rudy. Stop blaming everyone else. That's for amateurs.

RUDY

Well, she never could sing my songs.

IRENE

Don't worry, maestro, I can sing your songs. I can even sing the ones you stole them from.

HACKETT

Hold it, Irene. You know, Rudy, I know what Irene means about the love songs . . .

RUDY

Then let her write the show. I'm through.

IRENE

Rudy, listen. For your own sake.

153

RUDY

For my sake nothing. All you care about is yourself. Big star. Irene Lovelle. You're worried because you need this show . . . because out in Hollywood you can't even get yourself arrested. (IRENE *turns and starts off*) Gee, that was a lousy thing to say.

HACKETT
(*Going to* IRENE *and putting his arm around her*)
I'm sorry, Irene.

IRENE

It's all right, Dick. He's right. I do need this show. (*She looks at Rudy*) Rudy, maybe you just don't belong in the theater.

RUDY

Who the hell are you to tell me where I belong? (*To* HACKETT) And who the hell are you to tell me about songs? You had me mixed up there for a minute — but not now. I am Rudy Lorraine. I know songs. My stuff was great tonight, just great — perfect.

HACKETT
(*After a pause*)
Rudy, this is your first show. A lot of people on Broadway are wondering whether Rudy Lorraine can do a show. Tonight an audience told you something. You had better listen. Come on, honey.
(HACKETT *and* IRENE *go, his arm around her shoulder*)
(RUDY *slumps down on the sofa.* JACK *enters right, starts crossing towards his hat and coat*)

JACK
(*Impersonally*)
Good-by, Rudy.

154

RUDY

Jack, wait a minute.

JACK
(*Turns to look at him*)
What's the matter with you? You look terrible.

RUDY

I feel as if the roof fell in on me.

JACK

Well, it couldn't happen to a nicer fellow.
(*He starts off*)

RUDY

Where you going?

JACK

Where I said I was going. Stamford. I'm going to fix that book you said was ruining the whole show.

RUDY

I never said that.

JACK

The hell you didn't.

RUDY

Well, I didn't mean it. Why does everybody have to take me so seriously?

JACK

I guess maybe it's because of your charming manner.

RUDY

There ain't no room in the music business for a charming manner. I didn't think your book was bad. I just got mad because all you guys were jumping on my score.

JACK

I never said your score was bad. You know, Rudy, I never questioned your *talent*.

RUDY

Well, I've always thought you were a hell of a writer.

JACK

If we're so good, why are we in trouble?

RUDY
(*Like a kid*)

Why are we, Jack?

JACK
(*Thinking*)

I don't know. Maybe it's because this is the longest conversation you and I have ever had. We've never really gotten together.

RUDY

You're right.
(JACK *looks at him for a moment*)

JACK

On your feet. Let's go.

RUDY

Go where?

JACK

Stamford. We're going to go to work.

RUDY

Now wait a minute. I don't know if that's for me. I've always worked alone.

JACK

So do I, but this is one thing we've got to do together. If we're going to make our stuff fit, we've got to understand each other — get closer to each other.

RUDY

Please! I get enough of that stuff from Irene. She's always hacking away at that "closeness."

JACK

From Irene that's love talk. Rudy, I guess as a song writer you've written the word "love" about eighty million times. Do you know what it means?

RUDY

I ought to. I've had more dames . . .

JACK

That's not love; that's just exercise.

RUDY

If you're so big on this togetherness stuff, how come your wife walked out on you? (*Pause*) There I go with my big mouth again. (JACK *is thinking, not answering*) You mad at me?

JACK

No, I was just wondering why she did walk out. I guess I pushed her out. I stopped listening to her. Uncle Orville. Uncle Orville. She was hipped on Uncle Orville. Kept saying he would never leave the river. (*Stops*) Wait a minute, Rudy. I think she was right. Uncle Orville never would have left the river. I think Frankie's finally getting through to me.

RUDY

Well, did Orville leave the river, or didn't he?

JACK

In my novel he didn't. You know that.

RUDY

I never did read that book.

JACK

Well, you're going to come and read it now.

RUDY

Where?

JACK

Stamford. I've got about twenty copies.

RUDY

Twenty copies?

JACK

I only want you to read one. I've got an idea.

RUDY

What is it?

JACK

I don't know.

RUDY

I like it.

JACK

Let's get out of here.

(*They go*)

CLOSE IN

Scene Two

Stamford, breakfast room.
Rudy, seated at the table, is reading the book.

RUDY

This is great stuff, Jack — and your wife was right about the ending.

(JACK *enters carrying a coffee pot*)

JACK

She sure was. Our show has a phony finish and we're phony leading up to it. We've got to work backwards. (*Phone rings*) (*Starting for phone*) I'm beginning to see this. (*Phone rings again,* JACK *picks it up*) Hello.

(*Traveler pulls back and discloses half of the hotel suite in New Haven.* HACKETT *is on phone*)

HACKETT

Hello, Jack.

JACK

Hi, Dick. (*Quickly to* RUDY) It's Hackett.

HACKETT

Thought I'd call to check on your progress.

(TED *enters room as he says this*)

160

JACK	TED
Well I was stuck pretty bad for a while, Dick, but I got a hunch that now . . .	(*To* HACKETT) Rudy's gone! Left the hotel. Can't find him anywhere.

HACKETT

(*On phone*)

Hold it, Jack. (*To* TED) I'm talking to Jack.

TED

Let me talk to Jack, Dick.

RUDY

Let me talk to Dick, Jack.
    (HACKETT *and* JACK *give the phones to* TED *and* RUDY)

TED

(*On phone*)

Hello, Jack. That crazy, impossible Rudy Lorraine has vanished. Just walked out on us.

RUDY

If I were you, I'd sue the louse.

TED

That's just what I'm going to . . . (*Sudden take*) Who's this?

RUDY

It's the louse.

TED

What are you doing down there?

161

RUDY
(*Mildly*)

I'm down here working with my co-author Jack Jordan. (*He turns to* JACK) It's Ted.

JACK

Let me have it.
(*Takes phone*)

TED
(*To* HACKETT)

It's Rudy. He's down there with Jack. (*On phone*) Now listen here, Rudy. We can't fool around any more and . . .

JACK

Now, Teddy boy, take it easy.

HACKETT
(*Taking phone from* TED)

Let me have that. (*Into phone*) Rudy, this is Dick.

JACK

Dick, this is Jack.

TED
(*To* HACKETT)

Tell him to get the hell up here.

HACKETT

Jack, we really can't wait much longer getting to work. Should we have to postpone, we have to know about theaters and length of time.

162

SAY, DARLING

TED	JACK
(*Shouting*)	Dick, can you just give us
We can't postpone. What	more time? I think we've got
about the theater parties? We'll	an idea.
be in a hell of a mess.	

HACKETT
(*To* TED, *waving him down*)
SSSSShhhh. (*Then on phone*) What was that you said, Jack?

JACK
I said we've got an idea. I *think* it's an idea.

HACKETT
What is it?

JACK
I can't tell you yet. Give us forty-eight hours to work on it.
We'll be up there Friday afternoon to tell you what we've got.

HACKETT
Friday afternoon? All right.

JACK
Right.

TED
Let me have that phone. (HACKETT *hands him phone*) Now,
Jordan, I want one thing understood . . . Hello? Hello? (*Turns
to* HACKETT) He hung up on me.

163

HACKETT

That boy learns more every day.
(*Blackout in New Haven*)
(*After blackout in hotel, we go back to Stamford breakfast room*)

JACK

Now, musically, I think you've got to concentrate first on some kind of river number. Now I know there have been a lot of river songs — "Suwannee River," "Old Man River" . . .

RUDY

Don't worry. If Rudy Lorraine writes a river song, it'll top them all.

JACK

Well, I'm glad we haven't broken your spirit.

BLACKOUT

SCENE THREE

Hotel suite, New Haven.
Schatzie on phone. Maurice is playing the piano.

SCHATZIE

Hold it, Maurice. (MAURICE *stops*) (*On phone*) But, Sam . . .
now believe me, Sam, there's nothing to it. Sam, did I ever lie to
you? . . . Well, *this* time I'm telling the truth. (TED *enters from
bedroom*) Hold it. (*To* TED) It's Sam Zolotow from the *Times*.
He says he hears there's a lot of trouble on the show.

TED

Ridiculous. Let me have that. (*He takes phone*) Sam? How
are you, sweetheart? . . . Good. (*Listens for a moment*) Now
that's absolutely absurd. We are all working in complete harmony
without a single note of dissension . . . What? Certainly not.
Our authors have *not* left the show. They are working at Jordan's
place in Stamford. They'll be back here in New Haven this afternoon . . . Postpone? Why should we postpone? The show looks
great. No, Sam, we'll be coming in on time and we'll be coming
in with a winner . . . You're welcome, Sam. Glad to talk to you,
baby . . . Huh? Snow. Ted Snow. 'By. (*Hangs up, turns to*
SCHATZIE) Well, I think that he and I understand each other.

SCHATZIE

Sure. You both know you're lying.
(HACKETT *enters the room*)

165

TED

Oh, Dick, that was the New York *Times* on the phone, and I told them . . .

HACKETT
(*Cutting him off*)
Never mind that now. Ted, I want to get with you on some new dates. We'll have to move fast.

TED

New dates?

HACKETT
Yes. Now let's see. (*Counting on his fingers*) We close here Saturday, then we have three weeks in Boston. After that I want you to book two weeks in Philadelphia and two in Washington.

TED
(*Horrified*)
Dick, we can't postpone. I just told the *Times*.

HACKETT
(*Very certain*)
The boys have brought me what seems to be a feasible scheme for fixing the show . . .

TED
(*Interrupting*)
The boys? When did they get here?

HACKETT
They've been here since noon. Now, their scheme calls for a lot of work. Some new songs and . . .

TED

(*Interrupting again*)

Why wasn't I told when they came back? What am I around here?

HACKETT

I don't know what you are now, but when we called you at noon you were asleep.

TED

Where are Rudy and Jack now?

HACKETT

They're next door at the theater, running over some new stuff with Rex and Irene and some of the singers. They'll be up here in a few minutes and give you the whole works. They wanted to get it in good shape first.

TED

Schatzie, how do you feel about postponing — I mean, publicity-wise?

SCHATZIE

Well, I always say if you got a hit, it don't matter when you open, and then again, if you got a flop, it don't matter when you open either.

(JACK *and* RUDY *enter, followed by* IRENE, BORIS *and* PETER, *the piano player.* JACK *and* RUDY *are nervous and excited.* PETER *goes to the piano*)

JACK

Hi, Schatzie. Hi, Ted. The rest of the kids will be up in a minute.

IRENE
(*Looking at the manuscript*)
Rudy, I think this is very exciting.

JACK
Did Dick tell you what we've got?

TED
Nobody has told me anything, except about postponing, and, frankly . . .

HACKETT
Ted, sit down and listen to what the boys have done.

JACK
What we've done? What about you? You know, Ted, when Rudy and I came up here three hours ago, we had a few rough ideas and a couple of songs, and in about twenty minutes Richard Hackett put the whole thing together so it works. (*To* HACKETT) Dick, I'm beginning to learn a little bit about this business. And, Dick, when you learn a little bit about something, you develop a hell of a lot of respect for a guy who knows a lot.

HACKETT
Now cut that out. I've been forty-four years in this business and I do not intend at this stage of the game to have anyone treating me as though I were lovable. Now go on and give Ted the layout and let's have no more interruptions.

JACK
Come on in, kids, and make yourselves comfortable.
(KIDS *enter*)

TED

Now, look, if this is going to mean a lot of new scenery and costumes, I have my investors to think of . . .

HACKETT

No, Ted. That's what's good here. This change is only in basic thinking.

JACK

And the basic thinking is this . . . You see, Ted, we feel that this show cannot end with Orville going off with Rosie and the carnival. The audience feels cheated. Orville belongs on the river.

TED

But what happens to Rosie? Does she leave him?

IRENE

Don't look so sick. There's a happy ending.

JACK

Now in our scheme, we're only going to change those things that affect our new ending. Here's the way it will go: The first four scenes stay as is, including the husking bee. (*To* HACKETT) You know, that works. (*To* TED) But in scene five, we throw out Rosie's song and give Orville a ballad. Rudy . . .

RUDY

Well, you know Rosie, like most dames, is always trying to change Orville. And this ballad tells how he feels about it. It's an old song of mine that Irene always liked, and it seems to fit right here.

(*Sings*)
Try to love me just as I am.
Try to understand
That I can be much more than I am,
If you'll hold my hand.

For it makes you grow to know
You're loved for what you are;
So just the way I am
Please say you'll take me
And I can fly as high as the sky.
Your love will help me try.
Your love will help me try.

IRENE

I wouldn't mind losing five songs to get that one into the show.

JACK

You know, Ted, we were a little worried about Irene, because in this new version the part of Rosie is going to be cut way down. But she's been just wonderful about it . . .

IRENE

Now cut that out. Don't start making me sound lovable, either. I want this to be a big hit, because, as Rudy has often said, I need this show.

RUDY

I never said that.

IRENE AND JACK

The hell you didn't.

IRENE

Go ahead, Jack.

JACK

Our next change is at the end of the first act. It's that scene down on the river bank. In this one, Rosie, our tough carnival girl, needed a moment of real tenderness. And so Rudy came up with this waltz for Irene. Go ahead, Irene.

IRENE

But I've only taken a couple of looks at it.

RUDY

Never mind, sweetheart. Just sing it.

IRENE

Dance, dance, only with me,
Only with me in your arms.
Dance, dance, cling close to me,
Never to part.
Love, love, love only me,
All of our days from now on.
Dance . . . only with me
Till all our sweet music is gone.

RUDY

Come on, sing it, Rex!
(BORIS *swings* IRENE *into a waltz.* REX *sings*)

REX

Dance, dance, only with me,
Only with me near your heart.
Dance, dance, cling close to me,
Never to part.

171

IRENE

(*Stops dancing — takes up song*)
Love, love, love only me,
All of our days from now on.
Dance . . . only . . .

(REX *joins her in duet*)
. . . with me
Till all our sweet music is gone.
Dance with me
Only with meeeeeeeeee.

JACK

And that's going to end the first act.

TED

But that's a romantic number.

RUDY

That's right, because Rosie and Orville have not yet broken
up.

TED

(*Horrified*)
You mean you're going to end the first act without the lovers
breaking up?

HACKETT

You make it sound as though we were trying to overthrow the
government.

JACK

Ted, Orville and Rosie have their big breakup in the middle
of the second act, and they come together in our new finish. You

172

see, Ted, our show is really the story of *two* love affairs: one between Orville and Rosie, and one between Orville and a steamboat. Maybe you can't understand how anybody can love an
old coal-burning, cinder-throwing steamboat — well, old Orville
couldn't have understood what you all love about hanging
around cold theaters and drinking coffee out of paper cups.
Uncle Orville once said, "In the beginning God created heaven
and earth, and then He created steamboating." It's a wonderful
life, and Rosie learns about it in a song. This song is what this
show is about. Go ahead, Rudy.

RUDY

You do it. You know those words better than I do.

JACK

All right, but take it easy.

(JACK *starts the "River Song" and is joined by* RUDY,
IRENE, REX *and the others*)

You're standing on shore and you're watching the boats
A-steaming and puffing along,
You're hearing the sound of calliope notes
A-playing an old river song . . .
You're smelling the steam and the cylinder oil,
You're watching the work of a crew,
You're feeling the itch to get off the soil,
You've suddenly joined a crew, too . . .

ALL

'Cause something's always happening on the river,
On the river,
On the ri — i — i — ver.
Millions of tons of cargo to deliver;
Oh, the river is the only life for me.

173

JACK

(*Spoken*)

Hey, Keokuk — there's a great town!

RUDY

What's so great about it?

JACK

It's a river town, ain't it?

(*Sings*)

Along the Ohio from Pittsburgh on down
Till Cairo comes on into view.
The big Mississippi all muddy and brown
Then carries you up to St. Lou . . .
Then past Crazy Point the Missouri now flows
To Tarkeo and then to Squaw Bend.
To Omaha, then to Sioux City she goes,
You're now in Montana, my friend.

ALL

(*Singing chorus*)

'Cause something's always happening on the river,
On the river,
On the ri — i — i — ver.
Millions of tons of cargo to deliver;
Oh, the river is the only life for me.

(JACK *interrupts himself and starts talking — music under it*)

JACK

(*Spoken*)

Why, did you know Uncle Orville started out in West Virginia on the Monongahela and wound up clear out into the plains to

174

Fort Benton, Montana. That's Indian country and he scared the
buffalo half to death. Do you know how far that is? Three thousand six hundred and twenty-three miles, or as far as the New
York City piers to the docks in London, England, and he did it
all on an old beat-up steamboat right in the U.S.A., going west
and rolling all the way.

ALL

(*During chorus,* FRANKIE *enters*)

'Cause something's always happening on the river,
On the river,
On the ri — i — i — ver.
Millions of tons of cargo to deliver;
Oh, the river is the only life for me.

JACK

You think you'll quit sailing before it's too late,
And try some respectable jobs;
But somehow you find you're promoted mate,
Instructing a new bunch of slobs.
And then you're a captain, you find with alarm,

(*Sees* FRANKIE)

With kiddies and wife far away,

(*Spoken*)

Mr. Hackett, I'd like you to meet my wife.

(*Sung*)

You know you should get off and buy you a farm,
But you're on the river to stay.

ALL

'Cause something's always happening on the river,
On the river,
On the ri — i — i — ver.

175

Millions of tons of cargo to deliver.
Oh Monongahela
    Old Missouri
    Allegheny
    Mississippi
    Any river rolling to the sea.
Oh the river is the only life for me.
Ho!

(*After song* JACK *and* RUDY *are breathless. They look at* TED SNOW. TED *is silent for a moment*)

JACK
(*Breathless*)
Well? What do you think?

TED
I don't know. Tell it to me again.

BLACKOUT

Idlewild Airport. Stewardesses cross.

ANNOUNCEMENT

Flight Three-forty-five for Los Angeles ready to board in ten minutes.

(FRANKIE *enters, wearing a mink coat. She glances at her watch.* SCHATZIE *enters*)

SCHATZIE

Hey, Frankie.

FRANKIE

Hi, Schatzie.

SCHATZIE

Where's Jack?

FRANKIE

Back at the ticket counter.

SCHATZIE

(*Suddenly aware of the coat*)

Hey, he finally bought it for you, hanh? (FRANKIE *models the coat happily*) Well, it's about time he let loose of some of those royalties.

FRANKIE

He's been wanting to get me one for two years. *I* didn't want it. (*Snuggling into coat happily*) He had to force it on me.

SCHATZIE

Frankie, you look great in it. I want to pay you the highest compliment a guy can pay to a guy's wife. You don't look like a guy's wife. Hey, where you two going?

FRANKIE

I'm not going anywhere. Jack's going.
(JACK *enters*)

JACK

Schatzie!

SCHATZIE

Hi, Jack.

JACK

How are you, Schatzie? Long time.

SCHATZIE

Yeah. Where you going, Jack?

JACK

Los Angeles.

SCHATZIE

Los Angeles? What you going there for?

JACK

Well, you know that show I wrote. Those guys have some idea they want to make a picture out of it. Where you going?

SCHATZIE

I'm flying to Detroit tonight. Ted Snow has got a new one opening there.

JACK

Any good?

SCHATZIE

I don't know. A musical version of *The Brothers Katzaramoff*.

JACK

Karamazov.

SCHATZIE

Saying it right ain't going to help. (*He starts off*) Adios, Sweethearts, Adios.

JACK

'By, Schatzie. (SCHATZIE *goes*) Well, dear.

FRANKIE

Well, dear.

JACK

It's getting close to that time. I guess I better be getting down to the gate.

FRANKIE

You've got plenty of time. Now don't start getting nervous.

JACK

I'm not nervous.

FRANKIE

All right. You're not nervous. Did you get your ticket confirmed?

JACK
(*Suddenly clutching his pocket with his left hand*)
My ticket! I lost my ticket! (*Sees he is holding it in his other hand*) Oh. (*Puts ticket in pocket*) Well, maybe I am a little nervous. Damn it, this is my first movie and . . . Frankie, why don't you come with me?

FRANKIE

No, Jack.

JACK

Well, I guess you're right.

FRANKIE

I won that one pretty fast. (PILOT *enters, stops, stares at them.* FRANKIE *suddenly recognizes him*) Roy, the Boy Pilot!

PILOT
Frankie Jordan . . . Jack! How are you?
(*They all shake hands*)

JACK

Fine.

PILOT

You both look great.

JACK

So do you. How you doing?

PILOT

Swell. They got me pushing a DC-7 now. How about you?

JACK

I've been doing all right.

PILOT

(*Pointing to tickets in* JACK's *hand*)
Where you bound for?

JACK

I've been traded to the Dodgers.

FRANKIE

Well, it's about that show he wrote. They're going to make a movie of it.

PILOT

Is that a fact? I never did get to see that show. And I'm the guy who flew you down from Council Falls to write it.

FRANKIE

Well, it's not that show. You see, Jack did another show about the show.

JACK

Well, what I did was, after the first show, I wrote a book . . .

PILOT

You wrote a book *before* the show.

JACK

That was my first book. Then after that became a show, I wrote a book about doing the show . . . and then that book was made into another show, and now they're doing a movie which is based on the play from the book about the show. Well, Roy, it's been a living.

PILOT

Sounds okay. Well, some of us have to work.
(*He goes*)

ANNOUNCEMENT

Flight Three-forty-five for Los Angeles now loading at gate nine.

JACK

Well, honey . . .

FRANKIE

Well, dear . . . (*They kiss*) Take care of yourself.

JACK

Don't worry, honey, Uncle Orville will never leave the river.

CURTAIN

Date Due